STUDY GUIDE

BETTE KREUZ
University of Michigan, Dearborn

General, Organic, and Biological

CHEMISTRY

CONCISE | PRACTICAL | INTEGRATED

FROST

DEAL

Third Edition

Editor-in-Chief: Jeanne Zalesky

Executive Editor: Terry Haugen

Product Marketing Manager: Elizabeth Ellsworth

Project Managers: Elisa Mandelbaum and Mae Lum

Senior Acquisitions Editor: Scott Dustan

Program Manager: Lisa Pierce

Editorial Assistant: Fran Falk

Editorial Assistant: Lindsey Pruett

Marketing Assistant: Megan Riley

Associate Content Producer: Lauren Layn

Director of Development: Jennifer Hart

Development Editor: Donald Gecewicz

Team Lead, Program Management: Kristen Flathman

Team Lead, Project Management: David Zielonka

Full Service/Composition: Cenveo Publisher Services

Senior Project Manager: Mary Tindle, Cenveo Publisher Services

Associate Project Manager: Moumita Majumdar, Cenveo Publisher Services

Art Studio: Lachina, Kevin Kelsey

Text and Image Lead: Maya Gomez

Text and Image Permissions Researcher: Candice Velez, QBS

Design Manager: Marilyn Perry

Interior and Cover Designer: Elise Lansdon

Operations Specialist: Maura Zaldivar-Garcia

Front Cover Image: the food passionates/Corbis

Back Cover Image: Fotosearch LBRF/AGE Fotostock

www.pearsonhighered.com

1 2 3 4 5 6 7 8 9 10 - 16

ISBN-10: 0-134-16051-7; ISBN-13: 978-0-134-16051-1

Chemistry Basics— Matter and Measurement

Chapter Introduction

Learning Objectives
Upon completion of this material, a student should be able to do the following:
- A. Define the following key term:
    - **matter**

1.1 Classifying Matter: Mixture or Pure Substance

Learning Objectives
Upon completion of this material, a student should be able to do the following:
- A. Define the following key terms:

mixture	**element**
homogeneous mixture	**atom**
heterogeneous mixture	**compound**
pure substance	

- B. Classify matter as a pure substance or a mixture.
- C. Classify mixtures as homogeneous or heterogeneous.
- D. Classify pure substances as elements or compounds.

1.2 Elements, Compounds, and the Periodic Table

Learning Objectives
Upon completion of this material, a student should be able to do the following:
- A. Define the following key terms:

periodic table of the elements	**period**
chemical symbol	**chemical formula**
group	

- B. Distinguish between groups and periods.
- C. Locate metals and nonmetals on the periodic table.
- D. Identify the number of atoms of each element in a chemical formula.

1.3   Math Counts

Learning Objectives
Upon completion of this material, a student should be able to do the following:
   A.   Define the following key terms:

metric system	**equivalent units**
Système International d'Unités **(SI)**	**conversion factor**
kilogram	**dimensional analysis**
liter	**significant figures**
meter	**coefficient**
gram	

   B.   Convert between metric units.
   C.   Apply the appropriate number of significant figures to a measurement or calculation.
   D.   Convert numbers to scientific notation and scientific notation to numbers.
   E.   Convert numbers and fractions to percent and percent to numbers and fractions.

1.4   Matter: The "Stuff" of Matter

Learning Objectives
Upon completion of this material, a student should be able to do the following:
   A.   Define the following key terms:

mass	**joule**
weight	**calorie**
volume	**Calorie**
density	**heat**
specific gravity	**specific heat capacity**
temperature	**state of matter**
energy	**solid**
potential energy	**liquid**
kinetic energy	**gas**
conservation of energy	

   B.   Define mass and units for mass.
   C.   Define volume and units for volume.
   D.   Calculate and solve problems using density and specific gravity.
   E.   Convert temperatures among Celsius, Kelvin, and Fahrenheit.
   F.   Distinguish kinetic and potential energy.
   G.   Convert between energy units.
   H.   Define specific heat and compare values of various materials.
   I.   Contrast the properties of solids, liquids, and gases.

1.5 Measuring Matter

Learning Objectives
Upon completion of this material, a student should be able to do the following:
- A. Define the following key terms:

  accuracy   **drop factor**
  precision
- B. Distinguish between accuracy and precision.
- C. Convert SI or metric units and U.S. units.
- D. Apply conversion factors, units, drop units, and percent to measurements in health.

1.6 How Matter Changes

Learning Objectives
Upon completion of this material, a student should be able to do the following:
- A. Define the following key terms:

  physical change   **product**
  chemical reaction   **law of conservation of mass**
  chemical equation   **coefficient**
  reactant
- B. Distinguish between physical changes and chemical reactions.
- C. Balance a given chemical equation.

Practice Test for Chapter 1

1. Which of the following is a pure substance?
    A. copper wire
    B. a wooden baseball bat
    C. iced tea
    D. clean air

2. Which of the following statements about heterogeneous mixtures is **false**?
    A. The individual components are distinguishable.
    B. Components of the mixture can be separated by their physical properties.
    C. They are composed of two or more elements that are chemically joined together.
    D. No two samples contain the same substances in the same amount.

3. Which of the following is a mixture?
    A. muddy water
    B. table salt, NaCl
    C. oxygen, O_2
    D. aluminum foil

4. Which of the following is a compound?
    A. CO
    B. Cu
    C. Al
    D. Sn

5. What are the atomic symbols of silver and iron?
    A. Ag and Fe
    B. Au and Pb
    C. Si and I
    D. S and Ir

6. Which of the following elements is an alkaline earth metal?
    A. potassium
    B. strontium
    C. neon
    D. iodine

7. What main group element is located in Group 4A of Period 3 on the periodic table?
    A. Si
    B. Ga
    C. Ge
    D. In

8. Which of the following compounds contains six oxygen atoms?
    A. $C_6H_{12}O_6$
    B. $Mg(NO_3)_2$
    C. $Ca_3(PO_3)_2$
    D. all of the above

9. Which of the following compounds contains the element sodium?
    A. SO_2
    B. $NaNO_3$
    C. K_3PO_4
    D. Sm_2O_3

10. Length is measured in which of the following units?
    A. cc
    B. mg
    C. km
    D. cal

11. Which of the following is larger than 10 mg?
    A. 0.0000001 g
    B. 0.0001 kg
    C. 1 cg
    D. 10,000 µg

12. How many mL are in 0.0452 L?
    A. 45.2 mL
    B. 0.0000452 mL
    C. 4.52 mL
    D. 22.6 mL

13. In one second, light travels 29,979,245,800 cm. How many kilometers is this?
    A. 299,792.458 km
    B. 2,997,924,580 km
    C. 2,997,924,580,000,000 km
    D. 299,792,458,000 km

14. Which of the following has more than two significant figures?
    A. 20
    B. 1.20
    C. 430000
    D. 0.015

15. Perform the addition $53,511 + 4,200$ and report your answer to the correct number of significant figures.
    A. 58,000
    B. 57,700
    C. 57,711
    D. 49,300

16. Do the following calculation and report your answer to the correct number of significant figures.

$$0.00040 / 0.000000602 = ?$$

    A. 664.5
    B. 665
    C. 660
    D. 670

17. Express the following number in scientific notation.

0.0000416

   A. 4.16×10^{-5}
   B. 4.16×10^{5}
   C. 4.16×10^{-6}
   D. 416×10^{-3}

18. Express the following number in decimal format.

2.67×10^{4}

   A. 267
   B. 2,670
   C. 26,700
   D. 0.000267

19. Express 1/4 and 0.075 as percents, respectively.
   A. 4.0%, 7.5%
   B. 25%, 7.5%
   C. 25%, 75%
   D. 40%, 75%

20. An average adult requires an intake of 0.990 g of phosphorus per day. If a typical multivitamin tablet supplies 109 mg of phosphorus, what percent of the daily requirement does one tablet supply?
   A. 9.08%
   B. 0.110%
   C. 11.0%
   D. 908%

21. Mercury has a density of 13.6 g/mL. What is the mass in kilograms of 25.9 mL of mercury?
   A. 352 kg
   B. 1.90 kg
   C. 0.352 kg
   D. 0.00190 kg

22. A Sahara desert summer could be as hot as 133 °F. What is this temperature on the Kelvin scale?
   A. 329 K
   B. 133 K
   C. −217 K
   D. 13 K

23. A medium hardboiled egg is listed as containing 71 Cal. Calculate the number of joules in the egg.
   A. 7.1×10^{4} J
   B. 3.0×10^{5} J
   C. 1.5×10^{4} J
   D. 7.1×10^{-2} J

24. Consider the data given in this table taken from the text.

TABLE 1.5 Specific Heats of Various Substances	
Substance	Specific Heat (cal/g °C)
Water (liquid)	1.00
Human body	0.83
Paraffin wax	0.60
Wood, soft	0.34
Wood, hard	0.29
Air	0.24
Aluminum	0.21
Table salt	0.21
Brick	0.20
Stainless steel	0.12
Iron	0.11
Copper	0.092
Silver	0.056
Gold	0.031

For 1-g samples of each of the following substances, which will experience the smallest temperature change when 100 J of energy is added?
A. paraffin wax
B. air
C. stainless steel
D. gold

25. A liquid has _____.
A. neither definite shape nor volume
B. both definite shape and volume
C. a definite shape but no definite volume
D. a definite volume but no definite shape

26. The mass of an unknown was repeatedly measured, and the results are given below.

$$42.9 \text{ g}, \quad 42.8 \text{ g}, \quad 43.1 \text{ g}, \quad 43.0 \text{ g}$$

If the actual mass of the unknown is 50.0 g, this series of measurements is _____.
A. accurate but not precise
B. precise but not accurate
C. both accurate and precise
D. neither accurate nor precise

27. A patient needs 1500 mL of a fluid over a 12-hour period. The drop factor is 12 gtt/mL. What is the drip rate in drops per min (gtt/min)?
    A. 25 gtt/min
    B. 15 gtt/min
    C. 20 gtt/min
    D. 10 gtt/min

28. Which of the following is a physical change?
    A. rusting iron
    B. digesting food
    C. freezing water
    D. burning propane

29. Which of the following is a chemical change?
    A. boiling water
    B. making ammonia from nitrogen and hydrogen
    C. melting lead
    D. mixing salt with sand

30. How many reactant oxygen atoms will be present after balancing the equation for the following reaction?

$$C_2H_6O(l) + O_2(g) \rightarrow CO_2(g) + H_2O(g)$$

    A. 3
    B. 5
    C. 6
    D. 7

Answers

1. A   2. C   3. A   4. A   5. A   6. B   7. A   8. D   9. B   10. C
11. B   12. A   13. A   14. B   15. B   16. C   17. A   18. C   19. B   20. C
21. C   22. A   23. B   24. A   25. D   26. B   27. A   28. C   29. B   30. D

Chapter 1 – Solutions to Odd-Numbered Problems

Practice Problems

1.1   a. heterogeneous   b. homogeneous   c. homogeneous   d. heterogeneous

1.3   a. pure substance   b. mixture   c. pure substance

1.5   If it is found on the periodic table, it is an element.

        a. element   b. compound   c. element   d. compound

1.7   (answers in boldface)

Name	Elemental Symbol	Group	Period	Metal or Nonmetal
Fluorine	**F**	**7A**	**2**	**Nonmetal**
Lithium	**Li**	1A	2	**Metal**
Chlorine	Cl	**7A**	**3**	**Nonmetal**
Carbon	**C**	4A	2	Nonmetal

1.9   a. 1 sodium, 1 nitrogen, 2 oxygens

        b. 12 carbons, 22 hydrogens, 11 oxygens

        c. 1 calcium, 1 carbon, 3 oxygens

1.11   a. 2   b. 4   c. 5   d. 3

1.13   a. 2000   b. 54.5   c. 224,000   d. 132

1.15 $325 \ \cancel{mg} \times \dfrac{1 \ g}{1000 \ \cancel{mg}} = 0.325 \ g$

1.17   a. 2.03×10^8 b. 1.24×10^1 c. 2.78×10^{-8}

1.19   a. 0.0000156   b. 280,000   c. 0.090

1.21   a. 25%   b. 38%   c. 66%

1.23   a. 0.045   b. 0.130   c. 0.66   d. 0.78

1.25   a. 20   b. 90   c. 38   d. 133

1.27   a. less   b. more   c. less

1.29   39 g

1.31   446 mL

1.33   104.5 °F

1.35   Before eating, the food is mostly potential energy; during eating, it is a mixture of potential and kinetic energy as it is broken down; and after eating, it gets transformed into mostly kinetic energy to carry out the functions of the body.

1.37   86 cal

1.39   The warehouse made of pine. The pine has a higher specific heat, so it will take more heat energy to raise the temperature of the wood versus the brick. This will result in a slower transfer of the heat to the contents of the warehouse.

1.41   a. gas   b. solid

1.43   a. neither   b. both   c. good precision

1.45   150 g

1.47   100 mg/day; 50 mg/dose

1.49   37 drops/min or 37 gtt/min

1.51   5.0%

1.53   a. chemical reaction   b. physical change   c. chemical reaction

1.55   a. $1 + 1 \rightarrow 2$
       b. $2 + 1 \rightarrow 2$
1.57   a. $2Al(s) + 3Cl_2(g) \rightarrow 2AlCl_3(s)$
       b. $2HCl(aq) + Zn(s) \rightarrow ZnCl_2(aq) + H_2(g)$
       c. $SiO_2(s) + 3C(s) \rightarrow SiC(s) + 2CO(g)$

Additional Problems

1.59   a. mixture   b. mixture   c. mixture
       d. pure substance   e. pure substance
1.61   d. compound   e. element
1.63   a. homogeneous   d. homogeneous
1.65

Name	Element Symbol	Group	Period	Metal or Nonmetal
Nitrogen	**N**	**5A**	**2**	**Nonmetal**
Aluminum	**Al**	3A	3	**Metal**
Sulfur	S	**6A**	**3**	Nonmetal
Phosphorus	P	5A	3	**Nonmetal**

1.67. a. 1 titanium, 2 oxygens
       b. 1 nitrogen, 3 hydrogens
       c. 2 sodiums, 1 carbon, 3 oxygens
       d. 2 nitrogens, 1 oxygen
       e. 1 potassium, 1 oxygen, 1 hydrogen
1.69   a. smaller   b. larger   c. smaller   d. larger
1.71   a. 1000   b. 1   c. 1
       d. 10   e. 1,000,000
1.73   a. 50,000 strides   b. 30 mi (to 1 significant figure)
1.75   a. $\dfrac{1 \text{ raisin}}{1 \text{ g}}$

       b. 45 raisins
1.77   3.1 tablets or 3 tablets
1.79   a. 651,000   b. 0.00450   c. 6.67   d. 2000 (2.00×10^3)
1.81   Bag 2
1.83   385 L
1.85   700 g
1.87   24 °C
1.89   a. potential   b. kinetic   c. potential   d. potential
1.91 5.4×10^5 J
1.93   0.1 cal
1.95   The copper cookware. Copper has the lowest specific heat of the three metals. All other factors being equal, it will take the copper cookware the shortest time to heat up, which will result in a shorter overall cooking time and less energy use.
1.97   The gas particles contain more kinetic energy than the liquid particles because they are moving with higher velocities. In a gas, the particles are far apart and can move more freely.

1.99 Balance B is more accurate. Balance A is more precise.

1.101 Approximately 1.25 mL equals ¼ teaspoon in each dose.

1.103 42 drops/min

1.105 In a solid, the particles are packed together more rigidly than in a liquid; their movement is more limited in a solid.

1.107 a. chemical reaction   b. physical change   c. chemical reaction
d. chemical reaction   e. chemical reaction

1.109 a. $LiOH(s) + CO_2(g) \rightarrow LiHCO_3(s)$ (balanced)
b. $2HCl(aq) + Mg(s) \rightarrow MgCl_2(aq) + H_2(g)$
c. $2Fe(s) + 3S(s) \rightarrow Fe_2S_3(s)$

1.111 $O_2(g) + 2NO(g) \rightarrow 2NO_2(g)$

Challenge Problems

1.113 Because the density of healthy blood is greater than the density of the copper sulfate solution, healthy blood will drop to the bottom of the tube. This happens within a few seconds.

1.115 15 mL/h

1.117 a. compound. It contains more than one element in its formula (H_2O).
b. homogeneous. The sugar and water particles are evenly distributed when mixed.
c. physical change

Atoms and Reactivity

2.1 Atoms and Their Components

Learning Objectives

Upon completion of this material, a student should be able to do the following:

A. Define the following key terms:

subatomic particles	**nucleus**
proton	**electron cloud**
electron	**atomic mass unit (amu)**
neutron	

B. Name the kinds of subatomic particles that make up an atom.

C. Locate the subatomic particles in an atom.

2.2 Atomic Number and Mass Number

Learning Objectives

Upon completion of this material, a student should be able to do the following:

A. Define the following key terms:

atomic number	**mass number**

B. Distinguish atomic number and mass number.

C. Predict the mass number of an atom given the number of subatomic particles.

D. Determine the number of protons, neutrons, and electrons for an element given the mass number of symbolic notation.

E. Write symbolic notation for atoms when the number of protons and neutrons is given.

2.3 Isotopes and Atomic Mass

Learning Objectives

Upon completion of this material, a student should be able to do the following:

A. Define the following key terms:

isotopes	**atomic mass**

B. Define isotope.

C. Distinguish mass number and atomic number.

D. Predict the most common isotope based on the atomic mass of an element.

2.4   Radioactivity and Radioisotopes

Learning Objectives
Upon completion of this material, a student should be able to do the following:
- A. Define the following key terms:

nuclear radiation	radioactive
radioactive decay	radioisotope
alpha (α) particle	beta (β) particle
gamma (γ) ray	positron
ionizing radiation	sievert (Sv)
	millirem

- B. Define radioactivity.
- C. Distinguish the forms of ionizing radiation.
- D. Differentiate the penetrating power of the forms of ionizing radiation.
- E. Use biological exposure to radiation (Sv units) values to determine whether treatments are harmful.

2.5   Nuclear Equations and Radioactive Decay

Learning Objectives
Upon completion of this material, a student should be able to do the following:
- A. Define the following key terms:
    - nuclear decay equation
- B. Write a balanced nuclear decay equation for alpha, beta, gamma, and positron emissions.
- C. Write a balanced nuclear equation for the production of radioisotopes.

2.6   Radiation Units and Half-Lives

Learning Objectives
Upon completion of this material, a student should be able to do the following:
- A. Define the following key terms:

curie (Ci)	becquerel (Bq)
half-life	physical half-life
biological half-life	effective half-life

- B. Distinguish the units for radioactive emission and biological damage to tissue.
- C. Perform dosing calculations using radiation activity units.
- D. Determine the remaining dose of a radioactive isotope given the half-life.

2.7   Medical Applications for Radioisotopes

Learning Objectives
Upon completion of this material, a student should be able to do the following:
- A. Define the following key term:
    - tracer
- B. Apply the use of radioisotopes for the diagnosis and treatment of disease.

Practice Test for Chapter 2

1. A certain subatomic particle is located in the nucleus and has a relative mass of 1. This particle could have _____.
   A. no charge
   B. a positive charge
   C. a negative charge
   D. no charge or a positive charge

2. A subatomic particle with a large mass and a charge opposite that of an electron is represented by which of the following symbols?
   A. e^-
   B. p^+
   C. n^0
   D. n

3. A chemist uses an amu to measure _____.
   A. the charge of an electron
   B. the mass of an atom
   C. radiation penetrating power
   D. a mole of atoms

4. Most of the mass of an atom is located in _____.
   A. the electron cloud
   B. the neutrons
   C. the nucleus
   D. the protons

5. Consider the following symbolic notation.

   $$^{27}_{13}\text{Al}$$

   This isotope has _____.
   A. 13 protons, 13 electrons, and 27 neutrons
   B. 14 protons, 13 electrons, and 13 neutrons
   C. 27 protons, 13 electrons, and 13 neutrons
   D. 13 protons, 13 electrons, and 14 neutrons

6. An isotope has 29 protons, 29 electrons, and 36 neutrons. Which of the following is the correct symbolic representation?
   A. $^{36}_{29}\text{Cu}$
   B. $^{29}_{36}\text{Cu}$
   C. $^{65}_{36}\text{Cu}$
   D. $^{65}_{29}\text{Cu}$

7. Gallium (Ga) has two naturally occurring isotopes, gallium-69 and gallium-71. If the atomic mass of gallium is 69.72, this indicates that the abundance of gallium-69 _____.
   A. is greater than that of gallium-71
   B. is less than that of gallium-71
   C. is about the same as that of gallium-71
   D. A conclusion cannot be reached without more data.

8. The following represents one of the element blocks on the periodic table.

   The atomic mass of this element is _____.
   A. 26 amu
   B. 55.85 amu
   C. 81.85 amu
   D. 56 amu

9. The following represents one of the element blocks on the periodic table.

   | 17 |
   | Cl |
   | 35.45 |

   This element consists of two naturally occurring isotopes, chlorine-35 and chlorine-37. Which of the following correctly describes the isotopic composition of this element?
   A. The majority of any sample consists of chlorine-35.
   B. The majority of any sample consists of chlorine-37.
   C. Naturally occurring samples consist of about a 50:50 mixture of chlorine-35 and chlorine-37.

10. Which of the following types of radiation has the **least** penetrating power?
    A. α
    B. β
    C. $_{-1}^{0}e$
    D. γ

11. Which of the following types of radiation has a positive charge?
    A. α
    B. β
    C. $_{-1}^{0}e$
    D. γ

12. Which of the following types of radiation has approximately the same mass as a beta particle?
    A. α
    B. $_{0}^{0}\gamma$
    C. $_{1}^{0}e$
    D. $_{0}^{1}n$

13. Which of the following types of radiation is involved in positron emission tomography (PET)?
    A. α
    B. $^{0}_{0}\gamma$
    C. $^{0}_{1}e$
    D. Both $^{0}_{0}\gamma$ and $^{0}_{1}e$

14. Which of the following correctly describes the unit called a sievert (Sv)?
    A. A sievert is a unit used to measure the activity of a radioactive sample.
    B. A millirem is a larger unit that measures the same quantity as a sievert.
    C. Exposure to X-rays can be measured using sieverts.
    D. Exposure to 0.05 mSv can cause light radiation sickness.

15. Which of the following types of radiation will penetrate tissue and bone?
    A. α
    B. β
    C. X-rays
    D. γ

16. Wearing a laboratory coat would protect one from which of the following types of radiation?
    A. α
    B. β
    C. $^{0}_{-1}e$
    D. γ

17. A thick sheet of lead would **not** provide protection against the effects of which of the following types of radiation?
    A. α
    B. β
    C. $^{0}_{-1}e$
    D. γ
    E. A thick sheet of lead would provide protection against the effects of all of these types of radiation.

18. Which of the following equations could represent the preparation of a radioisotope in a laboratory?
    A. $^{234}_{91}Pa \longrightarrow {}^{234}_{92}U + {}^{0}_{-1}e$
    B. $^{58}_{26}Fe + {}^{1}_{0}n \longrightarrow {}^{59}_{26}Fe$
    C. $^{30}_{15}P \longrightarrow {}^{30}_{14}Si + {}^{0}_{1}e$
    D. $^{160}_{74}W \longrightarrow {}^{156}_{72}Hf + {}^{4}_{2}He$

19. An isotope containing 9 protons and 9 neutrons is used in PET scanning. Which of the following correctly characterizes this isotope?
    A. fluorine-18
    B. emits $_{1}^{0}e$
    C. mass number = 18
    D. A and C
    E. A, B, and C

20. When writing a nuclear decay equation, which of the following is correct?
    A. The sum of the mass numbers on either side of the equation must be the same.
    B. The sum of the atomic numbers on either side of the equation must be the same.
    C. The general form of the equation is: radioactive nucleus → new nucleus + radiation emission.
    D. All of these describe writing a correct nuclear decay equation.

21. Consider the following nuclear equation.

    $$_{29}^{66}\text{Cu} + _{-1}^{0}e \longrightarrow X$$

    In the equation, X is _____.
    A. $_{30}^{66}\text{Zn}$
    B. $_{28}^{66}\text{Ni}$
    C. $_{28}^{66}\text{Cu}$
    D. $_{29}^{65}\text{Cu}$

22. Consider the following nuclear equation.

    $$_{84}^{212}\text{Po} + X \longrightarrow _{86}^{216}\text{Rn}$$

    In the equation, X is _____.
    A. $_{2}^{4}\text{He}$
    B. $_{1}^{0}n$
    C. $_{1}^{0}e$
    D. $_{-1}^{0}e$

23. Consider the following nuclear equation.

    $$_{90}^{230}\text{Th} \longrightarrow _{90}^{230}\text{Th} + X$$

    In the equation, X is _____.
    A. $_{2}^{4}\text{He}$
    B. $_{1}^{0}n$
    C. $_{1}^{0}e$
    D. $_{-1}^{0}e$
    E. $_{0}^{0}\gamma$

24. An 8.0 mL sample of a radioactive isotope used in a diagnostic procedure contains 12 mCi; how many becquerels are present in the sample?
    A. 12 Bq
    B. 1.2×10^3 Bq
    C. 1.2×10^3 Bq
    D. 4.4×10^8 Bq
    E. 4.4×10^{14} Bq

25. An 8.0 mL sample of a radioactive isotope used in a diagnostic procedure contains 12 mCi. If the patient is to receive 2.8 mCi, what volume in milliliters should be injected?
    A. 8.0 mL
    B. 1.9 mL
    C. 0.67 mL
    D. 4.2 mL
    E. 12 mL

26. Which of the following statements is correct?
    A. The physical half-life is the amount of time it takes for 50% of the atoms in a radioactive sample to decay.
    B. The effective half-life and the biological half-life are affected by elimination from the body.
    C. The physical half-life is longer than the effective half-life.
    D. All of the above are correct except C.
    E. A, B, and C are correct.

27. Chromium-51 has a half-life of 28 days. If a 222 g sample is received in a clinical lab, how long will it take until only 27.8 g of radioactive chromium-51 remains?
    A. 28 days
    B. 3 days
    C. 56 days
    D. 84 days

28. Technicium-99m is a useful imaging tool for medical diagnosis. This isotope has a short half-life of 6 hours. If a patient receives a dose of 28 mCi, how much radioactivity will remain when the patient goes home 24 hours later?
    A. 4.0 mCi
    B. 7.0 mCi
    C. 3.5 mCi
    D. 1.8 mCi

29. A patient receives a 50 µCi dose of a gamma emitter. Which of the following is most likely correct?
    A. The gamma emitter is a tracer.
    B. The procedure is diagnostic in nature.
    C. The procedure is therapeutic in nature.
    D. A and B
    E. A and C

30. Consider the following data.

Radioisotope	Half-Life
Hydrogen-3	12.3 years
Iron-59	46 days
Iodine-131	8 days
Iodine-123	13.3 hours

Which isotope would be the **least** likely to be used in a medical application?
A. hydrogen-3
B. iron-59
C. iodine-131
D. iodine-123
E. All would be likely candidates.

Answers

1. D   2. B   3. B   4. C   5. D   6. D   7. A   8. B   9. A   10. A
11. A   12. C   13. D   14. C   15. D   16. A   17. E   18. B   19. E   20. D
21. B   22. A   23. E   24. D   25. B   26. E   27. D   28. D   29. D   30. A

Chapter 2 – Solutions to Odd-Numbered Problems

Practice Problems

2.1   Protons and neutrons are located in the nucleus (center) of an atom, and the electrons are found in a cloud outside of the nucleus called the electron cloud.

2.3   The mass of an electron is about 2000 times smaller than that of a proton.

2.5   a. The number of protons is the atomic number.
        b. The number of neutrons is the mass number minus the atomic number.
        c. The number of electrons is the same as the number of protons in an atom.

2.7   a. oxygen, O   b. magnesium, Mg   c. neon, Ne   d. copper, Cu
        e. silver, Ag

2.9   14

2.11   a. 35 protons, 45 neutrons, 35 electrons
        b. 11 protons, 12 neutrons, 11 electrons

2.13   a. $_2^4\text{He}$ b. $_{17}^{35}\text{Cl}$ c. $_{16}^{32}\text{S}$ d. $_{55}^{133}\text{Cs}$

2.15   a. 8 protons, 10 neutrons, 8 electrons
        b. 20 protons, 20 neutrons, 20 electrons
        c. 47 protons, 61 neutrons, 47 electrons
        d. 82 protons, 125 neutrons, 82 electrons

2.17   The isotope carbon-12 contains exactly 6 protons and 6 neutrons. The atomic mass as seen on the periodic table is an average mass, taking into consideration the abundance of all the carbon isotopes. Because about 1% of the carbon isotopes are carbon-13, the atomic mass is slightly higher than 12 amu.

2.19   a. Magnesium-24 has 12 neutrons, magnesium-25 has 13 neutrons, and magnesium-26 has 14 neutrons.
        b. $_{12}^{24}\text{Mg}$, $_{12}^{25}\text{Mg}$, $_{12}^{26}\text{Mg}$
        c. magnesium-24

2.21   An alpha particle is a helium nucleus. There are no electrons in an alpha particle.

2.23   gamma

2.25   6.2 mSv

2.27   0.5 – 1 Sv

2.29   a. $_6^{14}\text{C} \rightarrow _7^{14}\text{N} + _{-1}^{0}\text{e}$

        b. $_{84}^{212}\text{PO} \rightarrow _{82}^{208}\text{Pb} + _2^4\text{He}$

        c. $_{29}^{66}\text{Cu} \rightarrow _{30}^{66}\text{Zn} + _{-1}^{0}\text{e}$

        d. $_6^{11}\text{C} \rightarrow _5^{11}\text{B} + _1^0\text{e}$

2.31 $_{27}^{60}\text{Co} \rightarrow _{28}^{60}\text{Ni} + _{-1}^{0}\text{e}$

2.33   Sieverts measure the biological damage caused by radiation.

2.35   The half-lives are shorter, and they are prepared in the lab.

2.37 $50 \text{ mCi} \times \dfrac{20 \text{ mL}}{250 \text{ mCi}} = 4 \text{ mL}$

2.39 $48 \text{ h} \times \dfrac{\text{half} - \text{life}}{12 \text{ h}} = 4 \text{ half} - \text{lives}$

        $1.00 \text{ mCi} \times \dfrac{1}{2} \times \dfrac{1}{2} \times \dfrac{1}{2} \times \dfrac{1}{2} = 0.0625 \text{ mCi} = 62.5 \text{ } \mu\text{Ci}$

2.41   Ca-47 will concentrate in bone.

2.43 $40\,\mu Ci \xrightarrow[\text{1 half-life}]{} 20\,\mu Ci \xrightarrow[\text{2 half-lives}]{} 10\,\mu Ci \xrightarrow[\text{3 half-lives}]{} 50\,\mu Ci$

       After 3 half-lives (84 days), the patient will have less than 5 microCuries.

Additional Problems

2.45   a. neutron   b. protons   c. isotopes

2.47   a. 79 protons, 79 electrons

       b. 30 protons, 30 electrons

       c. 29 protons, 29 electrons

2.49   a. 26 protons, 29 neutrons, 26 electrons

       b. 7 protons, 8 neutrons, 7 electrons

       c. 24 protons, 28 neutrons, 24 electrons

       d. 56 protons, 81 neutrons, 56 electrons

2.51

Symbol	Number of Protons	Number of Neutrons	Number of Electrons	Mass Number	Name
$^{1}_{1}H$	**1**	**0**	**1**	**1**	**Hydrogen-1**
$^{24}_{12}Mg$	12	12	12	**24**	**Magnesium-24**
$^{9}_{4}Be$	**4**	5	**4**	9	**Beryllium-9**

2.53   a. alpha particle   b. beta particle   c. gamma radiation

2.55   a. $^{32}_{15}P$ b. $^{60}_{27}Co$ c. $^{51}_{24}Cr$

2.57 (answers in boldface)

Isotope Name	Symbolic Notation	Number of Protons	Number of Neutrons	Mass Number	Medical Use
Thallium-201	$^{201}_{81}Tl$	**81**	**120**	**201**	Tumor imaging
Iodine-123	$^{123}_{53}I$	53	**70**	**123**	Thyroid imaging
Xenon-133	$^{133}_{54}Xe$	54	79	133	Pulmonary ventilation imaging
Fluorine-18	$^{18}_{9}F$	**9**	**9**	**18**	Positron emission tomography (PET) imaging

2.59 $0.2\,Sv \times \dfrac{1000\,mSv}{Sv} \times \dfrac{scan}{0.0009\,mSv} = 222{,}222\ sacns\ or\ 200{,}000\ scans$

2.61 a. $^{15}_{8}\text{O} \rightarrow ^{15}_{7}\text{N} + ^{0}_{1}\text{e}$

b. $^{46}_{23}\text{V} \rightarrow ^{46}_{24}\text{Cr} + ^{0}_{-1}\text{e}$

c. $^{234}_{92}\text{U} \rightarrow ^{230}_{90}\text{Th} + ^{4}_{2}\text{He}$

d. $^{8}_{4}\text{Be} \rightarrow ^{4}_{2}\text{He} + ^{4}_{2}\text{He}$

2.63 a. $^{66}_{29}\text{Cu} \rightarrow ^{66}_{30}\text{Zn} + ^{0}_{-1}\text{e}$

b. $^{192}_{78}\text{Pt} \rightarrow ^{188}_{76}\text{Os} + ^{4}_{2}\text{He}$

c. $^{126}_{50}\text{Sn} \rightarrow ^{126}_{51}\text{Sb} + ^{0}_{-1}\text{e}$

d. $^{72}_{31}\text{Ga} \rightarrow ^{72}_{32}\text{Ge} + ^{0}_{-1}\text{e}$

2.65 $^{10}_{5}\text{B} + ^{4}_{2}\text{He} \rightarrow ^{12}_{7}\text{N} + 2^{1}_{0}\text{n}$

2.67 The becquerel (Bq) is the SI unit for measuring disintegrations per second from a radioactive material.

2.69 1.3 mL

2.71 1.95 mg

2.73 The isotope has undergone 3 half-lives based on:

$$80\text{mCi} \times \frac{1}{2} \times \frac{1}{2} \times \frac{1}{2} = 10 \text{ mci}$$

The half-life is then 2.7 d or 64 h based on:

$$\frac{8\,\text{d}}{3\,\text{half-lives}} = 2.7 \frac{\text{d}}{\text{half-life}} \text{ or } 64.8 \frac{\text{h}}{\text{half-life}} \approx 65\,\text{h}$$

2.75 A cold spot indicates a diseased area of an organ; a hot spot indicates an area of the organ where the cells are dividing rapidly or a cancerous growth.

Challenge Problems

2.77 1.56%

2.79 a. $^{18}_{8}\text{O} + ^{1}_{1}\text{p} \rightarrow ^{18}_{9}\text{F} + ^{1}_{0}\text{n} + ^{0}_{0}\gamma$

b. Because a person with a more active brain uses more glucose, more FDG will be present in the brain. The PET image would be brighter in more areas than for the normal person.

Compounds— How Elements Combine

Chapter
3

3.1 Electron Arrangements and the Octet Rule

Learning Objectives

Upon completion of this material, a student should be able to do the following:
- A. Define the following key terms:

  valence shell   **noble gases**
  valence electrons   **octet rule**
- B. Predict the number of valence electrons and energy levels for the main-group elements in the first four periods.
- C. Explain and apply the octet rule.

3.2 In Search of an Octet, Part 1: Ion Formation

Learning Objectives

Upon completion of this material, a student should be able to do the following:
- A. Define the following key terms:

  ions   **cation**
  anion   **polyatomic ion**
  isoelectronic
- B. Predict the ionic charge of a main-group element using the periodic table.
- C. Name ions given their symbol.
- D. Write symbols for ions given their name or the number of protons and electrons present.
- E. Gain familiarity with polyatomic ions and their charges.

3.3 Ionic Compounds—Electron Give and Take

Learning Objectives

Upon completion of this material, a student should be able to do the following:
- A. Define the following key terms:

  ionic bond   **ionic compound**
- B. Name ionic compounds given the formula.
- C. Give the formula and name of an ionic compound given the ions.
- D. Write the formula for ionic compounds given the name.
- E. Predict the ionic charges present in an ionic compound.

3.4   In Search of an Octet, Part 2: Covalent Bonding

Learning Objectives

Upon completion of this material, a student should be able to do the following:
- A. Define the following key terms:

    covalent bond

    covalent compound

    molecule

    bonding pair

    lone pair

    single bond

    double bond

    triple bond

    molecular formula

    Lewis structure

    binary compound

- B. Distinguish between ionic and covalent compounds.
- C. Establish the relationship between the number of valence electrons present in nonmetals in the Period 1–3 and the number of bonds that they typically make in a molecule.
- D. Draw Lewis structures for covalent compounds containing C, O, N, H, and the halogens (Group 7A).
- E. Name binary covalent compounds given the formula.
- F. Write the formula for a binary covalent compound given the name.

3.5   The Mole: Counting Atoms and Compounds

Learning Objectives

Upon completion of this material, a student should be able to do the following:
- A. Define the following key terms:

    mole

    molar mass

    Avogadro's number (N)

    equivalent units

    dalton

- B. Describe the mole unit and Avogadro's number.
- C. Calculate molar mass for a compound.
- D. Convert among the units of mole, number of particles, and gram.

3.6   Getting Covalent Compounds into Shape

Learning Objectives

Upon completion of this material, a student should be able to do the following:
- A. Define the following key terms:

    tetrahedral

    valence-shell electron-pair repulsion (VSEPR)

    charge clouds

    nonbonded pair

- B. Predict the molecular shapes of small molecules using VSEPR.
- C. Identify the location of a wedge and dash bonded atom in three-dimensional space.
- D. Predict the molecular shapes of atoms in Lewis structures.

3.7   Electronegativity and Molecular Polarity

Learning Objectives

Upon completion of this material, a student should be able to do the following:

A. Define the following key terms:

electronegativity	**polar molecule**
polar covalent bond	**nonpolar molecule**
nonpolar covalent bond	

B. Predict covalent bond polarity based on electronegativity.

C. Predict molecular polarity from bond polarities and molecular shape.

Practice Test for Chapter 3

1. Consider the following tables. The left column represents the energy level and the right column the number of electrons in that energy level. Which of the following represents the number of electrons in each energy level of magnesium?

    A.

N	Number of Electrons
1	8
2	2
3	

    B.

N	Number of Electrons
1	2
2	8
3	

    C.

N	Number of Electrons
1	2
2	8
3	2

    D.

N	Number of Electrons
1	2
2	8
3	12

2. How many valence electrons are there in an atom of phosphorus (P)?
    A. 3
    B. 5
    C. 15
    D. 16

3. An ion containing 38 protons and 36 electrons could be represented and named as _____.
    A. Sr^{2+}, strontium ion
    B. Kr^{2-}, kryptonide
    C. Sr^{2-}, strontide ion
    D. Kr^{2+}, krypton ion

4. Determine the correct formula of the ionic compound formed from the following combination of potassium ions and nitride ions.
   A. KN
   B. K_2N
   C. KN_3
   D. K_3N

5. The formula for barium carbonate is _____.
   A. BaC
   B. $BaCO_3$
   C. $Ba(HCO_3)_2$
   D. Ba_2C

6. Which of the following are, respectively, the correct name and composition of the ionic compound formed between ions of nickel(III) and sulfide?
   A. nickel(II) sulfide, 1 Ni^{2+} and S^{2-}
   B. nickel(III) sulfate, 3 Ni^{3+} and 2 SO_4^{2-}
   C. nickel(III) sulfide, 2 Ni^{3+} and 3 S^{2-}
   D. nickel(II) sulfate, 1 Ni^{2+} and SO_4^{2-}

7. The correct Lewis structure for OF_2 would contain _____.
   A. 1 O—F bond and 1 F—F bond
   B. 1 O=F bond and 1 F—F bond
   C. 2 O—F bonds
   D. 1 O—F bond and 1 F=O bond

8. If Cl atoms replaced the Br atoms in the molecule shown, which of the following would describe the new Lewis structure?

$$\ddot{B}r - \overset{\cdot\cdot}{\underset{\underset{\ddot{B}r}{|}}{P}} - \ddot{B}r$$

   A. There would be the same number of lone pairs.
   B. One of the bonds between P and Br would be double.
   C. P would no longer have a lone pair.
   D. The bonds would become ionic.
   E. All of the above

9. Based on Lewis structures, which of the following compounds is **not** likely to exist?
   A. CCl_4
   B. H_3S
   C. OCl_2
   D. PI_3

10. The correct name for P_2O_5 would be _____.
    A. diphosphorous pentoxide
    B. phosphorous oxide
    C. phosphorous(II) oxide
    D. pentaphosphorous dioxide

11. The formula for dinitrogen monoxide is _____.
    A. NO
    B. N_2O
    C. NO_2
    D. N_2O_3

12. What is the mass of 3.50 moles of sodium?
    A. 80.5 g
    B. 3.50 g
    C. 22.99 g
    D. 6.57 g

13. How many moles of platinum atoms are in 10.0 g of Pt?
    A. 195 mole of Pt
    B. 0.0513 mole of Pt
    C. 3.08×10^{22} mole of Pt
    D. 1950 mole of Pt

14. How many calcium atoms are in a beaker containing 22.5 g of Ca?
    A. 0.561 atoms
    B. 5.42×10^{26} atoms
    C. 1.07×10^{24} atoms
    D. 3.38×10^{23} atoms

15. Which of the following contains the largest number of atoms?
    A. 1.00 mole of K
    B. 1.00 mole of Li
    C. 1.00 mole of Na
    D. All contain the same number of atoms.

16. Which of the following contains the largest number of atoms?
    A. 5.00 g of copper
    B. 5.00 g of carbon
    C. 5.00 g of cesium
    D. All contain the same number of atoms.

17. What is the VSEPR form of the following molecule?

$$SO_3$$

    A. AB_2
    B. AB_3
    C. AB_2N_2
    D. AB_3N

18. What is the shape of a molecule of NBr_3?
    A. tetrahedral
    B. pyramidal
    C. trigonal planar
    D. bent

19. In which of the following molecules is the shape around each carbon atom tetrahedral?
    A.

    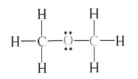

    B.

    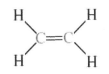

    C.

    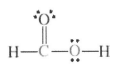

    D.

    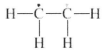

20. In which of the following bonds will the Br atom exist with a δ−?
    A. Br—O
    B. Br—F
    C. Br—N
    D. Br—Te

21. A student wrote the following as the Lewis structure for C_2H_4.

    H—C̈—Ċ—H
       | |
       H   H

    What error(s), if any, was(were) made?
    A. The number of atoms of C and H is incorrect.
    B. The H atoms do not form the correct number of bonds.
    C. The C atoms do not have an octet of electrons.
    D. All of the above are errors present in the structure.
    E. The structure is correct as written.

22. When using wedges and dashes to draw the three-dimensional nature of a structure on a piece of paper, which of the following correctly describes this type of representation?
    A. Bonds represented by simple lines lie with the plane of the paper.
    B. Bonds represented by wedges lie in front of the plane of the paper.
    C. Bonds represented by dashes lie behind the plane of the paper.
    D. All of the above correctly describe this type of representation.

23. Consider the representation of the following molecule.

    What would be the direction of the bond dipole of the Br attached by the wedge to the C?
    A. in front of the plane of the page with the arrow pointing backward
    B. in front of the plane of the page with the arrow pointing forward
    C. behind the plane of the page with the arrow pointing backward
    D. behind the plane of the page with the arrow pointing forward

24. In which of the following bonds will the dipole moment arrow (+━►) point toward N?
    A. N—S
    B. N—O
    C. N—Cl
    D. N—F

25. Which of the following molecules contains polar bonds?
    A. CI_4
    B. NCl_3
    C. OF_2
    D. All contain polar bonds.

26. The most polar bond among those listed would be _____.
    A. F—F
    B. O—F
    C. C—F
    D. N—F

27. Of the compounds listed, which would consist of nonpolar molecules?
   A.

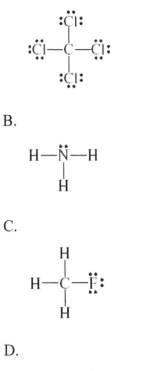

   B.

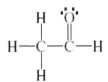

   C.

   H
   |
   H—C—F̈:
   |
   H

   D.

   H   Ö
   | ‖
   H—C—C—H
   |
   H

28. In the molecule shown here, how many of the carbon atoms have a trigonal planar shape?

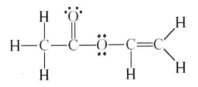

   A. 1
   B. 2
   C. 3
   D. 4
   E. none

29. For the following molecule, the arrow for the molecular dipole should be drawn as:

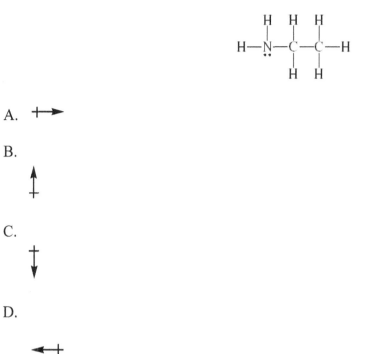

A.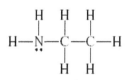

B.

C.

D.

E. The molecule does not have a dipole.

30. In the following structure, the shape around the N atom is _____.

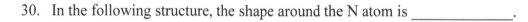

A. tetrahedral
B. pyramidal
C. trigonal planar
D. linear

Answers

1. C 2. B 3. A 4. D 5. B 6. C 7. C 8. A 9. B 10. A
11. B 12. A 13. B 14. D 15. D 16. B 17. B 18. B 19. A 20. D
21. C 22. D 23. B 24. A 25. D 26. C 27. A 28. C 29. D 30. B

Chapter 3 – Solutions to Odd-Numbered Problems

Practice Problems

3.1   a. 2 e^- in first energy level

      b. 2 e^- in first energy level, 4 e^- in second energy level

      c. 2 e^- in first energy level, 8 e^- in second energy level, 1 e^- in third energy level

      d. 2 e^- in first energy level, 8 e^- in second energy level

3.3   a. 6   b. 4   c. 5   d. 1

3.5   c. Ne

3.7   In atoms, the number of protons and electrons is the same, and there is no net charge. In a cation, there are more protons than electrons, giving the cation a positive charge.

3.9   In naming an anion, the last several letters of the nonmetal element name are dropped, and the suffix "ide" is applied.

3.11   a. 2+   b. 2-   c. 3-   d. 1+

3.13   a. 20 p, 18 e^- b. 53 p, 54 e^- c. 16 p, 18 e^- d. 30 p, 28 e^-

3.15   a. calcium ion   b. iodide   c. sulfide   d. zinc ion

3.17   a. fluoride, F^- b. chromium(III) ion, Cr^{3+}

3.19   a. ammonium   b. acetate   c. cyanide

3.21   a. $AuCl_3$, gold(III) chloride

      b. $CaSO_4$, calcium sulfate

      c. $Mg(OH)_2$, magnesium hydroxide

3.23   a. one Au^{3+}, three Cl^- b. one Ca^{2+}, one SO_4^{2-} c. one Mg^{2+}, two OH^-

3.25   a. sodium carbonate, Na_2CO_3

      b. iron(II) carbonate, $FeCO_3$

      c. aluminum carbonate, $Al_2(CO_3)_3$

3.27   a. two Na^+, one CO_3^{2-}

      b. one Fe^{2+}, one CO_3^{2-}

      c. two Al^{3+}, three CO_3^{2-}

3.29   (a)   (b)

      (c)   (d)

3.31

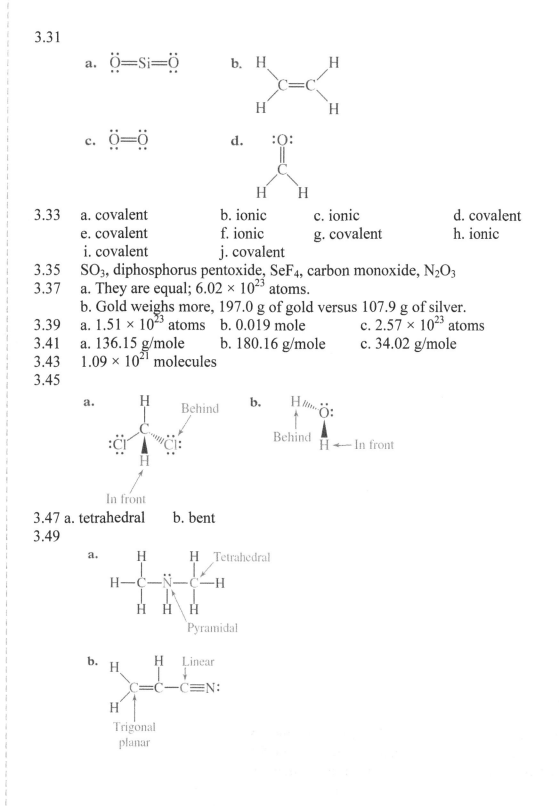

a. $\ddot{O}{=}Si{=}\ddot{O}$

b. (structure: H₂C=CH₂)

c. $\ddot{O}{=}\ddot{O}$

d. (structure: formaldehyde, :O: double bonded to C with two H)

3.33 a. covalent   b. ionic   c. ionic   d. covalent
e. covalent   f. ionic   g. covalent   h. ionic
i. covalent   j. covalent

3.35 SO_3, diphosphorus pentoxide, SeF_4, carbon monoxide, N_2O_3

3.37 a. They are equal; 6.02×10^{23} atoms.
b. Gold weighs more, 197.0 g of gold versus 107.9 g of silver.

3.39 a. 1.51×10^{23} atoms   b. 0.019 mole   c. 2.57×10^{23} atoms

3.41 a. 136.15 g/mole   b. 180.16 g/mole   c. 34.02 g/mole

3.43 1.09×10^{21} molecules

3.45

a. (structure: C bonded to H, H, :Cl, Cl: with "Behind", "In front" labels)

b. (structure: O with H, H, "Behind", "In front" labels)

3.47 a. tetrahedral   b. bent

3.49

a. (structure: H—C—N—C—H with H's; labels "Tetrahedral", "Pyramidal")

b. (structure: H₂C=C—C≡N: with labels "Linear", "Trigonal planar")

3.51

a. polar   H—Cl

Polar

Because this molecule contains one
bond, the bond and molecular dipoles
are the same.

b. polar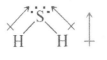

Polar

C–O bonds are polar and C–S bonds are not. The
molecular dipole is shown in orange.

c. polar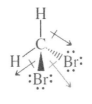

Polar

S–H bonds are polar. This molecule has a bent shape.
The lone pairs of electrons are on one side of the
molecule in three dimensions. The molecular dipole is
shown in orange.

d. polar

Polar

C–Br bonds are polar. Considering the tetrahedral shape,
the bromine side of the molecule is the negative side.
The molecular dipole is shown in orange.

Additional Problems

3.53   a. 2 electrons, Group 2A   b. 7 electrons, Group 7A
         c. 6 electrons, Group 6A   d. 5 electrons, Group 5A
         e. 2 electrons, Group 2A   f. 7 electrons, Group 7A
3.55   a. 4   b. 7   c. 1   d. 3
3.57   a. 4   b. 1   c. 1   d. 3
3.59   a. fewer   b. valence   c. positive
3.61   a. 17 p, 18 e⁻   b. 26 p, 23 e⁻   c. 24 p, 18 e⁻   d. 7 p, 10 e⁻
         e. 11 p, 10 e⁻   f. 1 p, 0 e⁻
3.63   b. iron(III)   c. chromium(VI)   d. nitride   f. hydrogen ion, also proton
3.65   a. lithium ion, Li+   b. bromide, Br⁻

3.67   a. Rubidium ion, Kr   b. Fluoride, Ne
        c. Sulfide, Ar   d. Calcium ion, Ar
3.69   a. $C_2H_3O_2^-$ b. HCO_3^- c. nitrate   d. cyanide
3.71   a. $(NH_4)_2S$ b. NH_4Cl c. $(NH_4)_2SO_4$ d. NH_4OH
3.73   a. Li_2CO_3 b. $KMnO_4$ c. NaI
3.75   a. sodium oxide   b. barium sulfate   c. copper(II) chloride
        d. magnesium nitrate   e. iron(III) oxide   f. potassium fluoride
3.77 1^-
3.79 $Na_2S_2O_5$
3.81   a. 4   b. 1   c. 3   d. 2
3.83   a. covalent, carbon tetrabromide
        b. covalent, silicon dioxide
        c. ionic, magnesium bromide
        d. covalent, nitrogen trichloride
        e. ionic, chromium(III) chloride
3.85   Ionic formulas are written for ionic compounds and use the smallest ratio of ions; molecular
        formulas are written for covalent compounds and indicate the exact number of atoms in the
        molecule.
3.87   a.

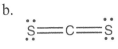

        b.

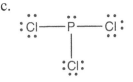

        c.

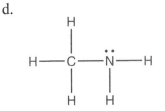

        d.

3.89   a. selenium dioxide
        b. silicon tetrafluoride
        c. tetraphosphorus trisulfide
        d. oxygen difluoride
3.91   A covalent bond results when two atoms share one or more pairs of electrons. An ionic bond is
        the attraction between two or more ions, which are formed by the loss and gain of electrons.
3.93   a. 101.10 g/mole   b. 90.08 g/mole   c. 46.07 g/mole
3.95   a. 16.0 g   b. 27.8 g   c. 404 g   d. 184 g
3.97 3×10^{17} atoms of carbon

3.99

a.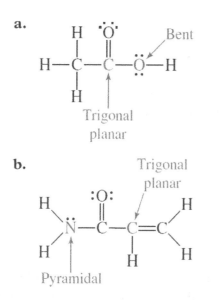

b.

3.101

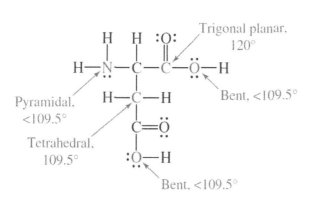

3.103

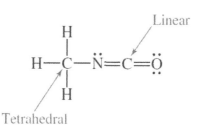

3.105 a. S   b. N   c. Cl   d. N

3.107

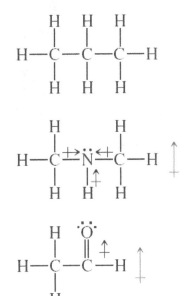

a. All bonds are nonpolar
b. Nonpolar

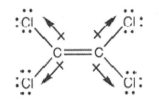

a. C–N bonds and N–H bond are polar
b. Polar, molecular dipole in orange

a. C=O bond is polar
b. Polar, molecular dipole in orange

Challenge Problems

3.109 $Ca_{10}(PO_4)_6(OH)_2$

3.111 9.60×10^{22} atoms of Pt

3.113 a. Lewis structure

b. Both carbons are trigonal planar, and the bond angle is 120°.

c. C—Cl bonds are polar, dipoles shown above.

d. The polar bonds are pulling outward equally and oppositely, so the molecule has no molecular dipole and is nonpolar.

Introduction to Matter and Measurement

Chapter Introduction

Learning Objectives
Upon completion of this material, a student should be able to do the following:
A. Define the following key terms:

 organic compounds   **organic chemistry**
 biomolecules   **inorganic compounds**

4.1 Representing the Structures of Organic Compounds

Learning Objectives
Upon completion of this material, a student should be able to do the following:
A. Define the following key terms:

 condensed structural formula   **skeletal structure**
B. Draw Lewis, condensed, and skeletal structures for organic compounds.

4.2 Alkanes: The Simplest Organic Compounds

Learning Objectives
Upon completion of this material, a student should be able to do the following:
A. Define the following key terms:

 alkane   **straight-chain alkane**
 saturated hydrocarbons   **cycloalkane**
B. Define the terms *saturated* and *unsaturated hydrocarbon*.
C. Name the first 10 straight-chain alkanes.
D. Compare the molecular formulas for straight-chain alkanes and cycloalkanes.
E. Draw skeletal and condensed structures for straight-chain alkanes, given the molecular formula, and vice versa.
F. Draw skeletal and condensed structures for cycloalkanes, given the molecular formula and vice versa.

4.3   Families of Organic Compounds—Functional Groups

Learning Objectives

Upon completion of this material, a student should be able to do the following:

A. Define the following key terms:

heteroatoms	aromatic compounds
functional group	aromaticity
carbonyl	resonance hybrid
carboxylic acid	monounsaturated
alkene	polyunsaturated
unsaturated hydrocarbons	fatty acids
terpenes	lipids
alkyne	saturated fatty acids

B. Characterize the unsaturated hydrocarbons alkenes, alkynes, and aromatics.

C. Identify common functional groups in organic molecules.

D. Draw saturated fatty acids in skeletal structure.

4.4   Nomenclature of Simple Alkanes

Learning Objectives

Upon completion of this material, a student should be able to do the following:

A. Define the following key terms:

branched-chain alkanes	halogen
alkyl groups	haloalkanes
substituent	

B. Draw branched-chain alkanes, haloalkanes, and cycloalkanes. Name them using IUPAC naming rules.

4.5   Isomerism in Organic Compounds

Learning Objectives

Upon completion of this material, a student should be able to do the following:

A. Define the following key terms:

isomer	unsaturated fatty acids
structural isomers	omega number
conformational isomer	essential fatty acids
conformers	enantiomer
stereoisomer	chiral
cis–trans stereoisomers	chiral center

B. Distinguish structural isomers from conformational isomers.

C. Identify cis and trans isomers in cycloalkanes and alkenes.

D. Draw unsaturated fatty acids in skeletal structure.

E. Locate chiral centers in organic molecules.

Practice Test for Chapter 4

1. When drawing a skeletal structure, which of the following is not a correct rule to follow?
    A. Carbon to carbon bonds are shown.
    B. Bonds between carbon and hydrogen are implied and not explicitly shown.
    C. Lone pairs of electrons are shown.
    D. Heteroatoms bonded to carbon are shown using their chemical symbol.
    E. Hydrogens bonded to heteroatoms are shown.

2. What is the molecular formula for the following structure?

    A. C_6H_{10}
    B. C_6H_{15}
    C. C_6H_8
    D. C_6H_{12}

3. Which of the choices does **not** represent the same molecule as shown here?

    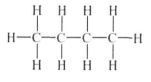

    A.

    B.

    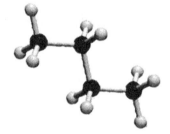

    C.

    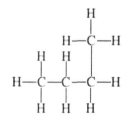

    D.

4. Which of the given terms does **not** describe the following structure?

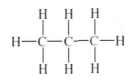

   A. hydrocarbon
   B. alkane
   C. nonpolar
   D. unsaturated

5. Which of the given formulas represents a skeletal structure?
   A. C_4H_{12}
   B.

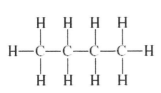

   C.

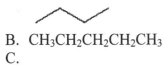

   D. $CH_3CH_2CH_2CH_3$

6. Pentane could be represented as:
   A.

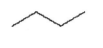

   B. $CH_3CH_2CH_2CH_2CH_3$
   C.

   D. C_6H_{14}

7. Identify the family of hydrocarbons present in each of the following, respectively.

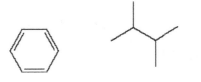

   A. aromatic, alkane, alkene
   B. alkene, alkane, alkyne
   C. aromatic, alkane, alkyne
   D. cycloalkene, alkane, alkyne

8. The fundamental feature that distinguishes an alkane from an alkene and from an alkyne is _____.
    A. the type of carbon-to-carbon bonds
    B. the presence of heteroatoms
    C. the presence of rings
    D. aromaticity

9. A molecule of a saturated organic compound contains an atom of bromine. This compound would be classified as a (n) _____.
    A. alkyne
    B. aldehyde
    C. haloalkane
    D. alkene
    E. aromatic

10. Identify, from left to right, the functional groups that contain a heteroatom in the following molecule.

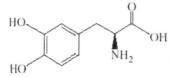

    A. alcohol, amine, carboxylic acid
    B. alcohol, amine, carboxylate
    C. phenol, amine, carboxylic acid
    D. phenol, amide, carboxylic acid

11. The members of the following pair are _____.

    A. not related
    B. structural isomers
    C. conformational isomers
    D. stereoisomers

12. The members of the following pair are _____.

CH₃CH₂CH₂CH₂CH₂CH₃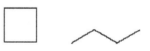

$CH_3CH_2CH_2CH_2CH_2CH_3$

$CH_3CH_2CH_2CHCH_3$
                |
               CH_3

    A. not related
    B. structural isomers
    C. conformational isomers
    D. stereoisomers

13. The members of the following pair are _____.

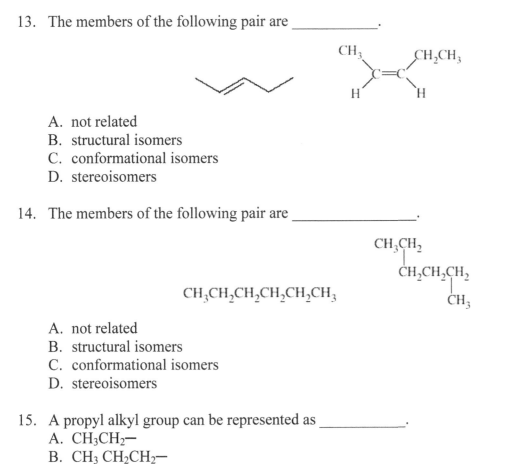

    A. not related
    B. structural isomers
    C. conformational isomers
    D. stereoisomers

14. The members of the following pair are _____.

$$CH_3CH_2CH_2CH_2CH_2CH_3$$

$$CH_3CH_2$$
$$|$$
$$CH_2CH_2CH_2$$
$$|$$
$$CH_3$$

    A. not related
    B. structural isomers
    C. conformational isomers
    D. stereoisomers

15. A propyl alkyl group can be represented as _____.
    A. CH_3CH_2-
    B. $CH_3\ CH_2CH_2-$
    C. $CH_3\ CH_2CH_2CH_2-$
    D. $CH_3CH_2CH_2CH_2CH_2-$

16. If the terms *iodo* and *dimethyl* are found in the name for an alkene, which of the following most likely characterizes this compound?
    A. It is unsaturated and contains a hetero atom and a CH_3- substituent.
    B. It is saturated and contains a hetero atom and two CH_3- substituents.
    C. It is unsaturated and contains two hetero atoms and a CH_3- substituent.
    D. It is unsaturated and contains a hetero atom and two CH_3- substituents.

17. The IUPAC name for the following compound is _____.

$$CH_3CH_2$$
$$|$$
$$CH_2CH_2CH_2CH_3$$

    A. 1-ethylbutane
    B. hexane
    C. 1-butylethane
    D. *trans*-1-ethylbutane

18. The IUPAC name for the following compound is _____.

$$CH_3CH_2\overset{\overset{\displaystyle CH_3}{|}}{\underset{\underset{\displaystyle CH_2CH_3}{|}}{C}}CH_2CH_3$$

A. 2,2-diethylbutane
B. 3,3-diethylbutane
C. 3-ethyl-3-methylpentane
D. 3-methyl-3-ethylpentane

19. The IUPAC name for the following compound is _____.

A. 2-fluoro-3-methylpentane
B. 2-fluoro-3-ethylbutane
C. 2-fluoroethylbutane
D. 4-fluoro-3-methylpentane

20. The IUPAC name for the following compound is _____.

$$CH_3CH_2\overset{\overset{}{}}{\underset{\underset{\displaystyle CH_3}{|}}{CH}}CH=CH_2$$

A. 3-methylpentane
B. 3-methylpentene
C. 3-methyl-1-pentene
D. 3-methyl-4-pentene

21. The IUPAC name for the following compound is _____.

A. *trans*-1-bromo-2-methylpentane
B. *cis*-1-bromo-2-ethylcyclopentane
C. *cis*-1-bromo-2-methylcyclopentane
D. *trans*-1-bromo-2-ethylcyclopentane

22. A compound with the name 2-chloro-4-methylpentane could be represented as:
    A. CH₃CHClCH₂CH(CH₃)CH₃

    A. $CH_3CHClCH_2CH(CH_3)CH_3$
    B.

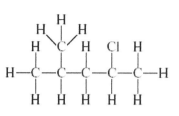

    C.

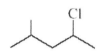

    D. B and C
    E. A, B, and C

23. Consider the following structure.

    This represents _____ .
    A. a fatty acid
    B. stearic acid [18:0]
    C. a lipid
    D. both A and B
    E. A, B, and C

24. The compound shown here would be classified as _____ .

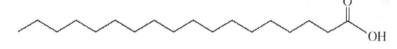

    A. saturated
    B. monounsaturated
    C. polyunsaturated
    D. essential

25. The correct carbon designation for the following fatty acid is _____ .

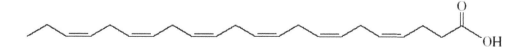

    A. [22:6], ω-3
    B. [6:22], ω-3
    C. [22:6], ω-6
    D. [21:6], ω-3

26. Which of the following pairs represents a set of enantiomers?
    A.

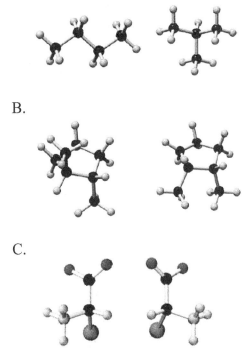

    B.

    C.

    D. B and C

27. In which type of isomer are the molecular formulas for the isomers different?
    A. conformational
    B. structural
    C. stereoisomers
    D. none of the above

28. How many chiral carbon atoms are present in the following molecule?

    A. 1
    B. 2
    C. 3
    D. 4
    E. 5

29. Which of the following molecules contains **more than one** chiral carbon atom?

A.

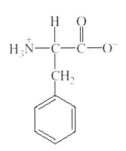

B.

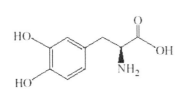

C.

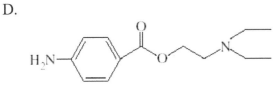

D.

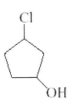

30. Which of the following does **not** describe a pair of enantiomers?
    A. biologically equivalent
    B. mirror images
    C. contain chiral carbon atoms
    D. "handed"

Answers

1. C   2. D   3. D   4. D   5. B   6. B   7. C   8. A   9. C   10. C
11. A   12. B   13. D   14. C   15. B   16. D   17. B   18. C   19. A   20. C
21. B   22. E   23. E   24. A   25. A   26. C   27. D   28. A   29. A   30. A

Chapter 4 – Solutions to Odd-Numbered Problems

Practice Problems

4.1   A Lewis structure shows all atoms, bonds, and nonbonding electrons. A condensed structure shows all atoms but as few bonds as possible.

4.3   Skeletal structures show bonds between carbon atoms. Since methane has only one carbon, it is not possible to draw its skeletal structure.

4.5

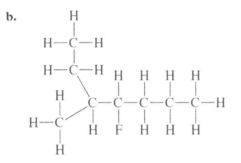

4.7

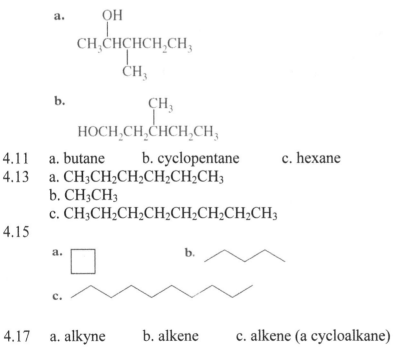

4.9

a.

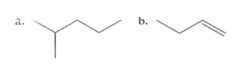

b.

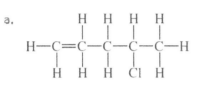

4.11   a. butane   b. cyclopentane   c. hexane

4.13   a. $CH_3CH_2CH_2CH_2CH_2CH_3$
       b. CH_3CH_3
       c. $CH_3CH_2CH_2CH_2CH_2CH_2CH_2CH_3$

4.15

a.   b.   c.

4.17   a. alkyne   b. alkene   c. alkene (a cycloalkane)

4.19

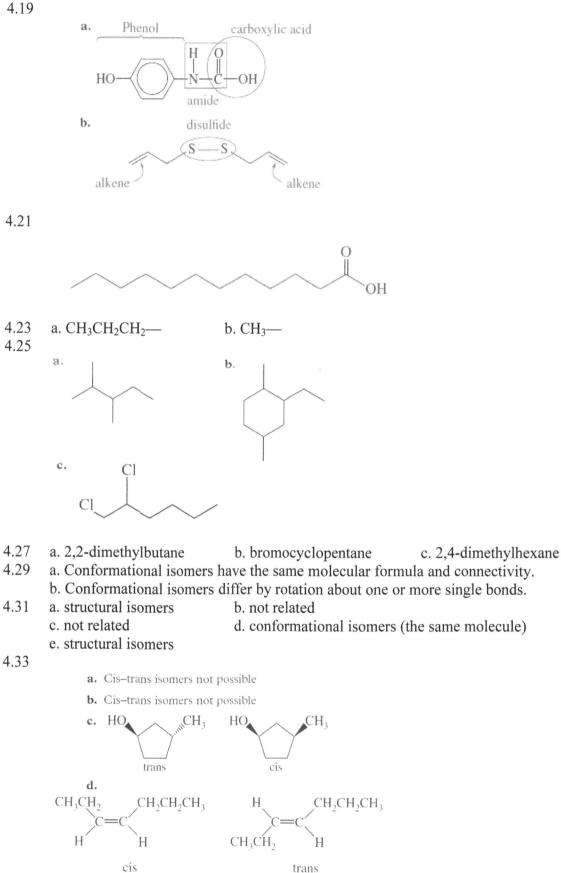

a.   Phenol   carboxylic acid

HO—⟨benzene ring⟩—N—C—OH

        H O
        amide

b.   disulfide

alkene   S—S   alkene

4.21

4.23   a. CH₃CH₂CH₂—   b. CH₃—

4.25   a.   b.

        c.   Cl

        Cl

4.27   a. 2,2-dimethylbutane   b. bromocyclopentane   c. 2,4-dimethylhexane
4.29   a. Conformational isomers have the same molecular formula and connectivity.
        b. Conformational isomers differ by rotation about one or more single bonds.
4.31   a. structural isomers   b. not related
        c. not related   d. conformational isomers (the same molecule)
        e. structural isomers
4.33
        a. Cis–trans isomers not possible
        b. Cis–trans isomers not possible
        c. HO   CH₃   HO   CH₃

                trans   cis

        d.
        CH₃CH₂   CH₂CH₂CH₃   H   CH₂CH₂CH₃
            C=C   C=C
        H   H   CH₃CH₂   H

            cis   trans

4.35

a.
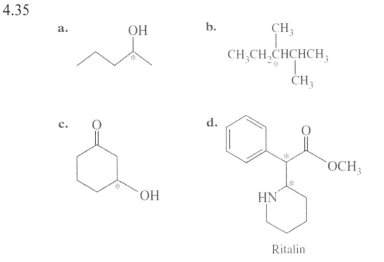

b.
CH₃
|
CH₃CH₂CHCHCH₃
‑ *|
CH₃

c.

d.

Ritalin

Additional Problems

4.37

a. CH₃CH₂CH₂CH₃   b. CH₃CH₂CH₂OH
c. CH₃CH₂CH₂CH₂CH₂CH₂CH₃

4.39

a.

b.

c.

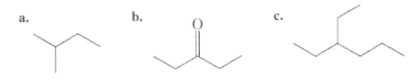

4.41

a. CH₃CH(OH)CH₂CH₃
b. CH₃CH₂CH₂Br
c. CH₃CH₂COOH

4.43

a.

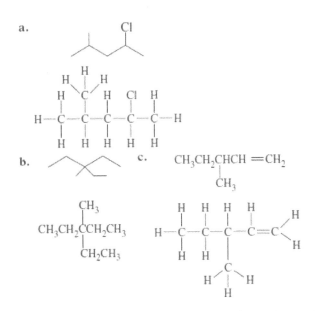

b.

c.   CH₃CH₂CHCH ═CH₂
|
CH₃

CH₃
|
CH₃CH₂CCH₂CH₃
|
CH₂CH₃

4.45 Hydrocarbons are organic compounds composed only of hydrogen and carbon. Saturated refers to the fact that each carbon is bonded to the maximum number of hydrogens.

4.47

a. butane,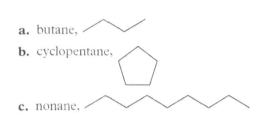

b. cyclopentane,

c. nonane,

4.49 a. cyclobutane   b. heptane

4.51 An unsaturated fatty acid contains one or more carbon–carbon double bonds, but a saturated fatty acid contains no double bonds.

4.53

a.

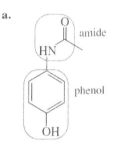

amide

HN

phenol

OH

Acetaminophen

b.

alcohol

OH   O

carboxylate

$+N$ O^-

amine   Carnitine
(quaternary)

4.55 A = protonated amine,   B = sulfide (thioether),   C = ether,   D = amine (tertiary)

4.57

$CH_3CH_2CHCH_2CH_2CH_3$

a. CH_2CH_3

CH_3

$CH_3CH_2CCH_2CH_2CH_2CH_3$

b. Cl   Cl

CH_3

$CH_3CHCHCHCH_2CH_2CH_2CH_3$

c. CH_3 $CHCH_3$

CH_3

4.59

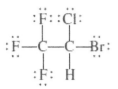

4.61

$CH_3CH_2CH_2CH_2CH_2CH_3$

4.63

There are four possible isomers

Cyclopentane   Methylcyclobutane   1,2-Dimethylcylopropane

1,1-Dimethylcylopropane

4.65

Butane   2-Methylpropane

4.67

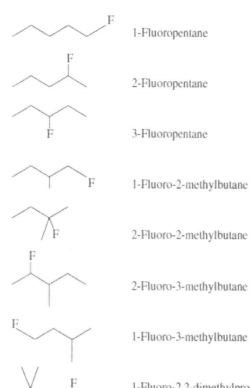

1-Fluoropentane

2-Fluoropentane

3-Fluoropentane

1-Fluoro-2-methylbutane

2-Fluoro-2-methylbutane

2-Fluoro-3-methylbutane

1-Fluoro-3-methylbutane

1-Fluoro-2,2-dimethylpropane

4.69

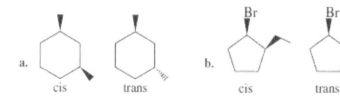

a.   cis   trans

b.   cis   trans

4.71

a. no cis–trans isomer

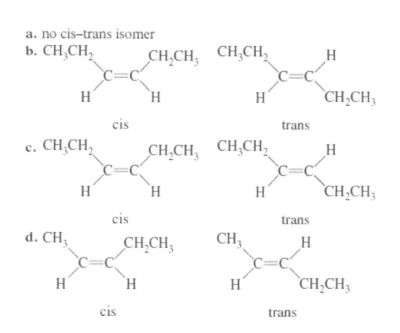

b. CH₃CH₂ ... CH₂CH₃   CH₃CH₂ ... H

cis   trans

c. CH₃CH₂ ... CH₂CH₃   CH₃CH₂ ... H

cis   trans

d. CH₃ ... CH₂CH₃   CH₃ ... H

cis   trans

4.73 a. cis   b. cis   c. trans   d. trans

4.75 linoleic acid, [18:2], ω-6

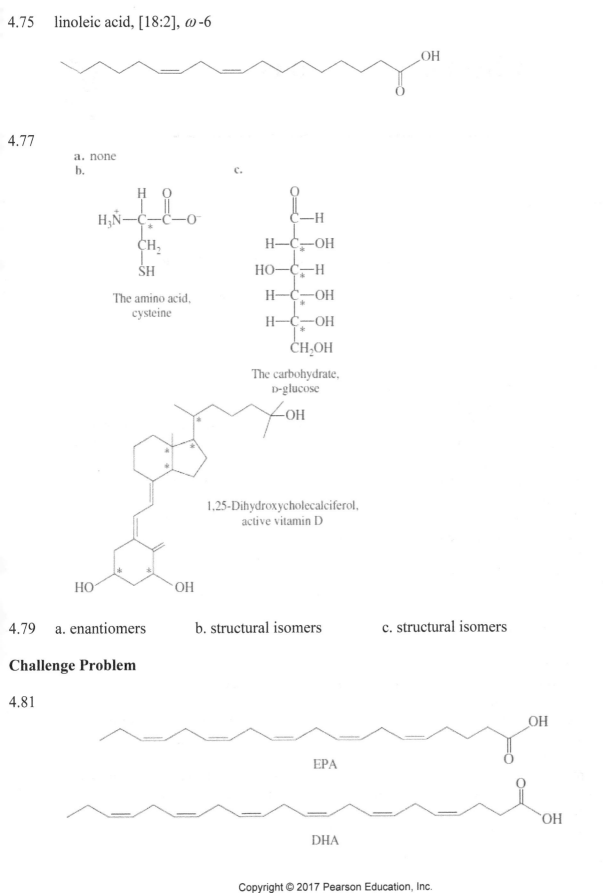

4.77

a. none
b.   c.

The amino acid,
cysteine

The carbohydrate,
D-glucose

1,25-Dihydroxycholecalciferol,
active vitamin D

4.79 a. enantiomers   b. structural isomers   c. structural isomers

Challenge Problem

4.81

EPA

DHA

Chemical Reactions

Chapter Introduction

Learning Objectives
Upon completion of this material, a student should be able to do the following:
- A. Define the following key terms:

    thermodynamics　　　　　　　　　　　**reaction kinetics**

5.1　Thermodynamics

Learning Objectives
Upon completion of this material, a student should be able to do the following:
- A. Define the following key terms:

exothermic reactions	**spontaneous processes**
endothermic reactions	**nonspontaneous processes**
free energy (G)	**ATP**
free energy change (ΔG)	**activation energy**
exergonic	**calorimeter**
endergonic	**combustion**

- B. Predict spontaneity of a reaction based on the ΔG value.
- C. Draw reaction energy diagrams for exergonic and endergonic reactions.
- D. Apply understanding of how a calorimeter works.
- E. Calculate the energy content in foods from its nutrient molecules.

5.2　Chemical Reactions: Kinetics

Learning Objectives
Upon completion of this material, a student should be able to do the following:
- A. Define the following key terms:

rate of reaction	**biochemical reactions**
catalyst	**active site**
enzyme	

- B. Predict relative activation energies and speed of reactions using a reaction energy diagram.
- C. Determine the effect that temperature, amount of reactants, and a catalyst have on the rate of a reaction.
- D. Describe how enzymes are biological catalysts.

5.3   Overview of Chemical Reactions

Learning Objectives
    Upon completion of this material, a student should be able to do the following:
    A. Define the following key terms:

synthesis reactions	**irreversible reactions**
decomposition reactions	**reaction mechanism**
exchange reactions	**hydrogenation**
reversible reactions	**glycolysis**
chemical equilibrium	**ADP**

    B. Classify reactions as synthesis, decomposition, or exchange reactions.
    C. Predict the products of a synthesis, decomposition, or exchange reaction.
    D. Distinguish reversible and irreversible reactions.
    E. Predict the products and balance the chemical equation for a hydrocarbon undergoing combustion.
    F. Contrast a general chemical equation and an organic chemical equation.

5.4   Oxidation and Reduction

Learning Objectives
    Upon completion of this material, a student should be able to do the following:
    A. Define the following key terms:

oxidation	**reducing agent**
reduction	**oxidizing agent**
cellular respiration	

    B. Identify the substance oxidized and the substance reduced in an inorganic oxidation–reduction reaction.
    C. Identify the substance oxidized and the substance reduced in an organic oxidation–reduction reaction.
    D. Predict the products of an organic oxidation or a reduction reaction.

5.5   Organic Reactions: Condensation and Hydrolysis

Learning Objectives
    Upon completion of this material, a student should be able to do the following:
    A. Define the following key terms:

condensation	**carboxylation**
dehydration	**phosphorylation**
hydrolysis	**dephosphorylation**

    B. Predict the products of an organic condensation reaction.
    C. Predict the products of an organic hydrolysis reaction.
    D. Identify organic reactions as oxidation, reduction, condensation, or hydrolysis.

5.6   Organic Addition Reactions to Alkenes

Learning Objectives

Upon completion of this material, a student should be able to do the following:

    A. Define the following key terms:

        addition to alkenes   **Markovnikov's rule**
        hydration

    B. Predict the products of a hydrogenation reaction, an addition reaction of an alkene.

    C. Predict the products of a hydration reaction, an addition reaction of an alkene.

Practice Test for Chapter 5

1. Consider the following reaction energy diagram.

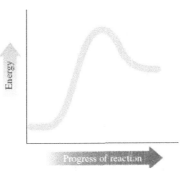

   Which of the following correlates with the reaction represented in the diagram?
   A. positive ΔG
   B. nonspontaneous
   C. endergonic
   D. all of the above

2. Consider the following reaction energy diagram.

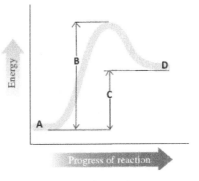

   Which letter represents the energy of reaction?
   A. A
   B. B
   C. C
   D. D

3. Consider the following reaction energy diagram.

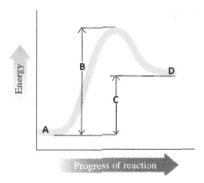

Which quantity shown in the diagram would change if a catalyst were added to this reaction?
A. A
B. B
C. C
D. D
E. Both B and C would change.

4. Consider the following reaction energy diagram.

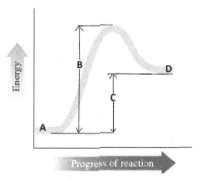

For this reaction, what approximate relationship would exist between the energy of the reaction and the activation energy?
A. The energy of reaction and the activation energy are about the same.
B. The energy of reaction is about double the activation energy.
C. The energy of reaction is about half the activation energy.
D. The energy of reaction is about one quarter the activation energy.
E. The energy of reaction is about four times the activation energy.

5. Butter turning rancid is an example of an oxidation reaction with atmospheric oxygen. Which of the following would not decrease the rate of this reaction?
A. placing the butter in a closed container
B. storing the butter in an atmosphere of nitrogen
C. putting the butter in a refrigerator at 40 °F
D. All of these actions will decrease the rate at which rancidity occurs.

6. Which of the following is the most likely to represent an equilibrium reaction?
   A. snow melting when the air temperature is 32 °F
   B. butane from a disposable lighter burning
   C. nitroglycerin causing an explosion
   D. digestion of protein found in food
   E. None of these is an equilibrium reaction.

7. Which of the following characterizes any spontaneous reaction?
   A. ΔG has a positive value.
   B. Reactants and products are separated in the reaction by the type of arrow shown below.

   C. Reaction requires the presence of a catalyst.
   D. The energy content of the products is greater than that of the reactants.
   E. None of the above characterizes a spontaneous reaction.

8. Consider the following descriptions. Which describes a reaction that is exothermic and exergonic?
   A. A spontaneous reaction produces heat as it occurs.
   B. A nonspontaneous reaction produces heat as it occurs.
   C. A spontaneous reaction requires heat to proceed.
   D. A nonspontaneous reaction requires heat to proceed.

9. Consider the following set of reaction conditions.

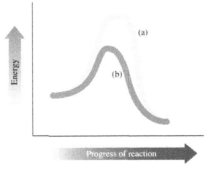

   Which of the following is correct about the accompanying reaction?
   A. The reaction is endergonic.
   B. The reaction would be enzyme-catalyzed.
   C. The reaction would occur in a biochemical pathway.
   D. All of the above are correct.

10. Consider the following reaction energy diagram.

   Based on this diagram, which of the following statements is (are) correct?
   A. Curve b represents the uncatalyzed pathway.
   B. Curve a represents the catalyzed pathway.
   C. An exothermic reaction is represented.
   D. Curve b has the higher activation energy.
   E. None of the statements are correct.

11. Consider the following two reaction energy diagrams.

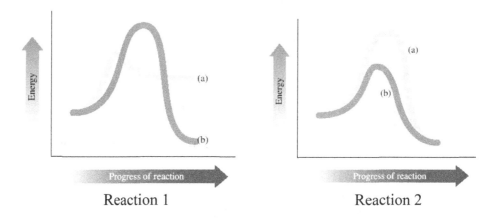

Reaction 1   Reaction 2

If the energy scale is the **same** in both diagrams, which is the fastest exothermic reaction?
A. Reaction 1, pathway a
B. Reaction 1, pathway b
C. Reaction 2, pathway a
D. Reaction 2, pathway b

12. A can of microwaveable soup has the following nutritional facts on the label.

22 g fat
30 g carbohydrate
6 g protein

If there are two servings per container, to two significant figures, approximately how many Calories are there in one serving?
A. 170 Cal
B. 340 Cal
C. 110 Cal
D. 260 Cal

13. Which of the following correctly ranks the type of nutrient molecules in order of increasing energy content?
A. protein < fat < carbohydrate
B. protein ≈ carbohydrate < fat
C. fat < protein ≈ carbohydrate
D. carbohydrate < protein < fat
E. carbohydrate ≈ fat < protein

14. What type of reaction is represented by the following chemical equation?

$$2KClO_3(s) \rightarrow 2KCl(s) + 3O_2(g)$$

A. exchange reaction
B. equilibrium reaction
C. decomposition reaction
D. synthesis reaction

15. The following is a graphic representation of the reaction of a polymer and its monomers.

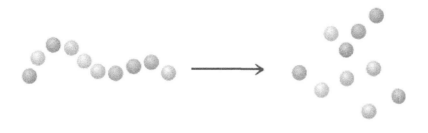

This reaction would be classified as a(n) _____.
A. exchange reaction
B. equilibrium reaction
C. decomposition reaction
D. synthesis reaction

16. What is (are) the most likely product(s) of the following synthesis reaction?
$$Ca(s) + Cl_2(g) \rightarrow$$
A. $CaCl_2$
B. $CaCl$
C. $CaI + C$
D. $Ca + I_2 + C$

17. What is (are) the most likely product(s) of the following exchange reaction?
$$BaF_2(aq) + K_2S(aq) \rightarrow$$
A. $BaS + 2\ KF$
B. $F_2S + K_2Ba$
C. $BaKS + F_2$
D. $K_2F_2S + Ba$

18. In the complete combustion of pentane (C_5H_{12}), how many molecules of oxygen are used?
A. 6
B. 5
C. 8
D. 3
E. 2

19. An oxidation reaction may involve _____.
A. loss of electrons
B. loss of hydrogen
C. gain of oxygen
D. A, B, and C
E. neither A, nor B, nor C.

20. Consider the following reaction.

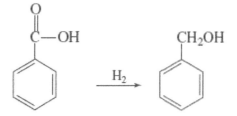

Which of the following statements correctly describes this reaction?
A. The organic reactant is oxidized.
B. The organic reactant is the reducing agent.
C. The product of the reaction is an alcohol
D. All of the above characterize this reaction.

21. Which of the following changes would represent a reduction?
A. Mg forms MgO in air.
B. Cu^{2+} ions form Cu_2O during a laboratory sugar test.
C. The biomolecule NADH forms NAD^+.
D. CH_3OH forms HCOOH.
E. All represent reductions.

22. What type of reaction is shown in the following equation?

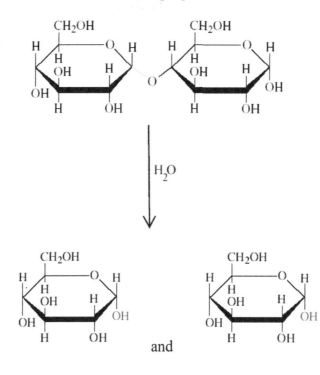

A. condensation
B. hydrolysis
C. oxidation
D. reduction

23. What type of reaction is shown in the following equation?

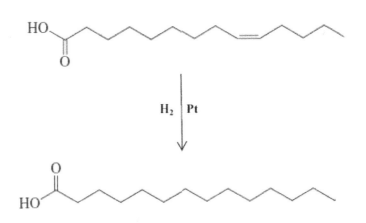

A. condensation
B. hydrolysis
C. oxidation
D. reduction
E. hydration

24. What type of reaction is shown in the following equation?

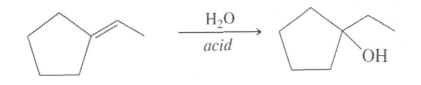

A. condensation
B. hydrolysis
C. oxidation
D. reduction
E. hydration

25. What type of reaction is shown in the following equation?

A. condensation
B. hydrolysis
C. oxidation
D. reduction
E. hydration

26. Of the reaction conditions shown in the choices, which represents the appropriate reaction condition to carry out the following conversion.

$$CH_3CH_2CH=CHCH_3 \longrightarrow CH_3CH_2CH_2CH_2CH_3$$

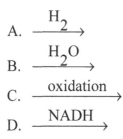

A. $\xrightarrow{H_2}$

B. $\xrightarrow{H_2O}$

C. $\xrightarrow{\text{oxidation}}$

D. $\xrightarrow{NADH}$

27. Which statement characterizes the following reaction?

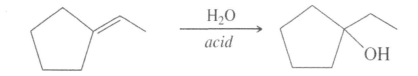

A. The product shown is not that predicted by Markovnikov's rule.
B. The reaction is an example of an addition reaction.
C. The reverse reaction is a hydrolysis reaction.
D. The water would serve as a catalyst.
E. All of the above characterize this reaction.

28. What is the major organic product of the following reaction?

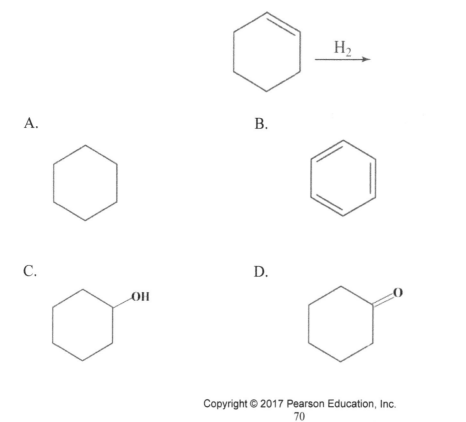

A.

B.

C.

OH

D.

O

29. The following structure represents the product of a reaction with hydrogen in the presence of a Pt catalyst.

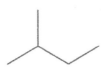

Which of the following could be used as a reactant in this reaction?

A.   B.   C.

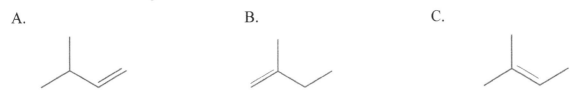

D. either A or C
E. A, B, or C

30. The following structure represents the product of a reaction with water in the presence of an acid catalyst.

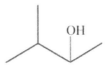

Which of the following could be used as a reactant in this reaction?

A.

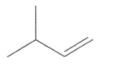

B.

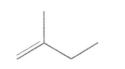

C.

D. either A or C
E. A, B, or C

Answers

1. D 2. C 3. B 4. C 5. D 6. A 7. E 8. A 9. D 10. C
11. D 12. A 13. B 14. C 15. C 16. A 17. A 18. C 19. D 20. C
21. B 22. B 23. D 24. E 25. C 26. A 27. B 28. A 29. E 30. A

Chapter 5 – Solutions to Odd-Numbered Problems

Practice Problems

5.1 Cold. If the reaction is endothermic, it absorbs heat from its surroundings, which cools the reaction. This reaction would have a $-\Delta G$ because it is spontaneous.

5.3 a. exothermic   b. endothermic

5.5 a. spontaneous   b. spontaneous

5.7 The pistachio nut since it produced less energy when burned, as evidenced by the smaller temperature change.

5.9 135 calories (rounds to 100 calories —1 significant figure)

5.11 a. Increasing the temperature increases the rate by increasing the velocity of the reactant molecules. The faster they move, the more likely they are to collide and react.
 b. Increasing the concentration of the reactant increases the likelihood of collision and increases the rate of the reaction.

5.13 The concentration of reactants decreases as the reaction progresses, so the rate slows.

5.15 activation energy

5.17 a. decrease   b. increase   c. increase

5.19 a. exchange   b. decomposition   c. synthesis

5.21 a. irreversible   b. irreversible   c. reversible

5.23 $2C_2H_6(g) + 7O_2(g) \rightarrow 4CO_2(g) + 6H_2O(g)$

5.25 In both organic and biochemical reactions, the structure of the organic molecule is shown. The yields arrow shows reversibility for both. Also, changes in the structure of functional groups are shown.

5.27 a. reduction   b. oxidation   c. oxidation

5.29 Hydrogen is oxidized, and oxygen is reduced.

5.31 Pyruvate is reduced to lactate; NADH is oxidized to NAD$^+$.

5.33

$$\overset{\displaystyle O}{\overset{\displaystyle \|}{H_3C-C}}-OCH_2CH_3 + H_2O$$

5.35

a.

$$H_3C-\overset{\displaystyle H_3C}{\underset{\displaystyle H}{C}}-\overset{\displaystyle CH_3}{\underset{\displaystyle H}{C}}-H$$

b.

c.

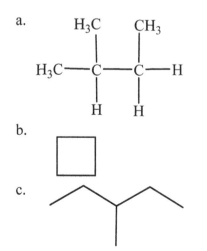

5.37

a.

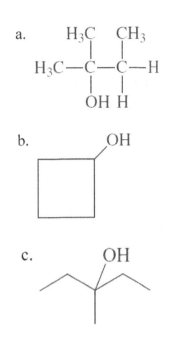

b.

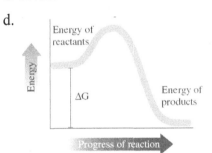

c.

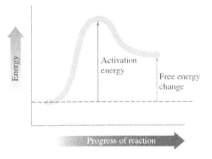

Additional Problems

5.39   a. exothermic   b. reactants   c. Yes, it is spontaneous.

d.

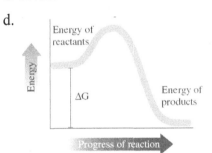

5.41   An exergonic reaction with a low-activation energy occurs faster. The low-activation energy allows the reactants to react more quickly.

5.43   a. Curve (a) is faster, curve (b) is slower.
b. Curve (a) is endergonic, curve (b) is exergonic.
c. (b) is a spontaneous reaction.
d. (a) has a positive ΔG.

5.45

5.47 780 calories (rounds to 800 calories)

5.49   a. $Mg(s) + Cl_2(g) \rightarrow MgCl_2(s)$

      b. $2HI(g) \rightarrow H_2(g) + I_2(g)$

      c. $Ca(s) + Zn(NO_3)_2(aq) \rightarrow Zn(s) + Ca(NO_3)_2(aq)$

      d. $K_2S(aq) + Pb(NO_3)(aq) \rightarrow PbS(s) + 2KNO_3(aq)$

5.51   a. condensation   b. oxidation

5.53 $C_5H_{12}(g) + 8\ O_2(g) \rightarrow 5\ CO_2(g) + 6\ H_2O(g)$

5.55   a. Copper is oxidized, and silver is reduced.

      b. Aluminum is oxidized, oxygen is reduced.

      c. Bromide is oxidized, silver is reduced.

5.57   **a.**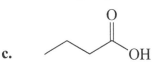

      b. $HOCH_2CH_2CH_3$

      c.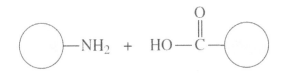

5.59

5.61   **a.**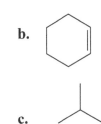

      b.

      c.

5.63   **a.**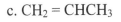

      b.

      c. $CH_2 = CHCH_3$

5.65   a. The forward reaction (glucose to glycogen) is condensation; the reverse reaction (glycogen to glucose) is hydrolysis.

      b. On a low-carbohydrate diet, glycogen stores are depleted, and a significant amount of water is also lost. So the weight lost is not fat but rather glycogen and water.

Challenge Problems

5.67   60 days

5.69

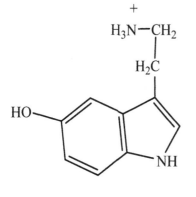

Serotonin

Carbohydrates: Life's Sweet Molecules

Chapter Introduction

Learning Objectives
Upon completion of this material, a student should be able to do the following:
- A. Define the following key term:
  - **carbohydrates**

6.1   Classes of Carbohydrates

Learning Objectives
Upon completion of this material, a student should be able to do the following:
- A. Define the following key terms:

monosaccharides	**polysaccharides**
disaccharides	**soluble fiber**
oligosaccharides	**insoluble fiber**

- B. Classify carbohydrates as mono-, di-, oligo-, or polysaccharides.
- C. Distinguish soluble and insoluble fiber.

6.2   Functional Groups in Monosaccharides

Learning Objectives
Upon completion of this material, a student should be able to do the following:
- A. Define the following key terms:

alcohol	**ketone**
primary (1°) alcohol	**aldose**
secondary (2°) alcohol	**ketose**
tertiary (3°) alcohol	**glucose**
	fructose
aldehyde	

- B. Distinguish primary, secondary, and tertiary alcohols.
- C. Recognize and draw the functional groups alcohol, aldehyde, and ketone.

6.3 Stereochemistry in Monosaccharides

Learning Objectives

Upon completion of this material, a student should be able to do the following:
A. Define the following key terms:

Fischer projection	**glycolysis**
D-sugar	**galactose**
L-sugar	**epimers**
diastereomer	**mannose**

B. Distinguish D- and L- stereoisomers of monosaccharides.
C. Draw Fischer projections of linear monosaccharides.
D. Define enantiomer, epimer, and diastereomer.
E. Draw enantiomers and diastereomers of linear monosaccharides.
F. Characterize common monosaccharides.

6.4 Reactions of Monosaccharides

Learning Objectives

Upon completion of this material, a student should be able to do the following:
A. Define the following key terms:

hemiacetal	**furanose**
anomers	**Benedict's test**
anomeric carbon	**reducing sugar**
pyranose	

B. Draw cyclic α and β anomers from linear monosaccharide structures.
C. Draw oxidation and reduction products of aldoses.

6.5 Disaccharides

Learning Objectives

Upon completion of this material, a student should be able to do the following:
A. Define the following key terms:

glycoside	**lactose**
glycosidic bond	**sucrose**
maltose	

B. Distinguish condensation and hydrolysis reactions of simple sugars.
C. Locate and name glycosidic bonds in disaccharides.
D. Characterize common dissacharides.
E. Apply the sweetness scale to various sweet products.

6.6 Polysaccharides

Learning Objectives

Upon completion of this material, a student should be able to do the following:
A. Define the following key terms:

storage polysaccharides	**glycogen**
structural polysaccharides	**cellulose**
amylose	**chitin**
amylopectin	

B. Identify polysaccharides by glycosidic bond and sugar subunit.

6.7 Carbohydrates and Blood

Learning Objectives

Upon completion of this material, a student should be able to do the following:
A. Define the following key terms:

fucose	**glycoaminoglycans**
heparin	

B. Predict ABO compatibility.
C. Describe the structure and role of heparin.

Practice Test for Chapter 6

1. The following structure could be the representation of a(n) _____.

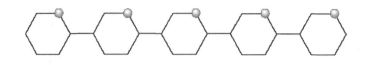

    A. monosaccharide
    B. disaccharide
    C. oligosaccharide
    D. polysaccharide

2. Which of the following characterizes insoluble fiber?
    A. found in carrots
    B. lowers blood cholesterol
    C. prevents constipation
    D. can slow the absorption of blood sugar
    E. All are characteristics of insoluble fiber.

3. The molecule represents epinephrine (adrenaline). Epinephrine contains _____.

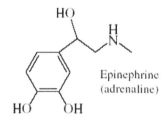

Epinephrine
(adrenaline)

    A. one primary alcohol substituent
    B. one secondary alcohol substituent
    C. three secondary alcohol substituents
    D. one tertiary alcohol substituent

4. Which of the following contains a ketone functional group?

A.

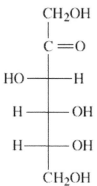

$$CH_2OH$$
$$C=O$$
$$HO \longrightarrow H$$
$$H \longrightarrow OH$$
$$H \longrightarrow OH$$
$$CH_2OH$$

B.

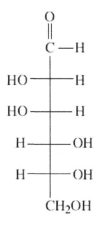

$$O$$
$$C-H$$
$$HO \longrightarrow H$$
$$HO \longrightarrow H$$
$$H \longrightarrow OH$$
$$H \longrightarrow OH$$
$$CH_2OH$$

C.

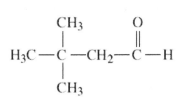

$$CH_3 \qquad O$$
$$H_3C-C-CH_2-C-H$$
$$CH_3$$

D.

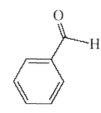

5. How many chiral centers are in the following monosaccharide?

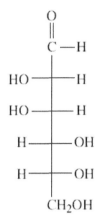

A. 2
B. 3
C. 4
D. 5
E. 6

6. In a Fischer projection, the difference between the D-sugar and the L-sugar is the

_____.
A. presence of an aldehyde versus a ketone functional group
B. number of chiral centers
C. position of the —OH group closest to the carbonyl atom
D. position of the —OH group furthest from the carbonyl carbon atom
E. position of the —OH group on the chiral center furthest from the carbonyl carbon atom

7. Which of the following would be classified as an aldohexose?

A.

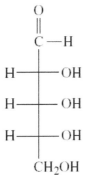

B.

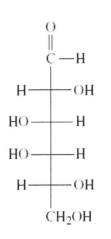

C.

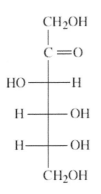

D. None of these is an aldohexose.

8. Which of the following represents the L-sugar of an aldose?

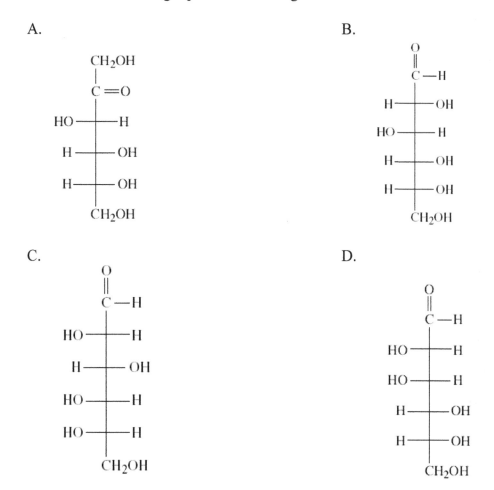

A.

CH$_2$OH
|
C=O
HO——H
H——OH
H——OH
CH$_2$OH

B.

O
‖
C—H
H——OH
HO——H
H——OH
H——OH
CH$_2$OH

C.

O
‖
C—H
HO——H
H——OH
HO——H
HO——H
CH$_2$OH

D.

O
‖
C—H
HO——H
HO——H
H——OH
H——OH
CH$_2$OH

E. None of these is the L-sugar of an aldose.

9. Which of the following represents an enantiomer of:

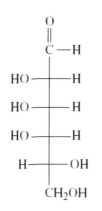

A.

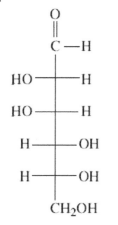

B.

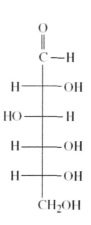

C.

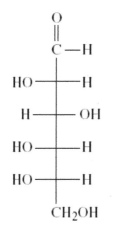

D.

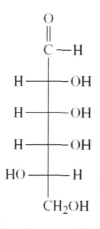

E. None of these is an enantiomer.

10. Which of the following represents an epimer of:

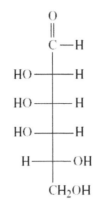

$$\begin{array}{c} O \\ \| \\ C-H \end{array}$$

HO———H

HO———H

HO———H

H———OH

CH₂OH

A.

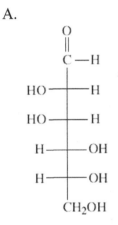

$$\begin{array}{c} O \\ \| \\ C-H \end{array}$$

HO———H

HO———H

H———OH

H———OH

CH₂OH

B.

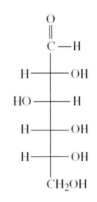

$$\begin{array}{c} O \\ \| \\ C-H \end{array}$$

H———OH

HO———H

H———OH

H———OH

CH₂OH

C.

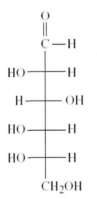

$$\begin{array}{c} O \\ \| \\ C-H \end{array}$$

HO———H

H———OH

HO———H

HO———H

CH₂OH

D.

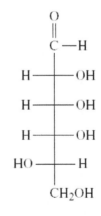

$$\begin{array}{c} O \\ \| \\ C-H \end{array}$$

H———OH

H———OH

H———OH

HO———H

CH₂OH

E. None of these is an epimer.

11. Which of the following represents a diastereomer of:

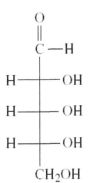

A.

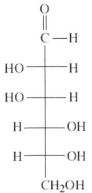

B.

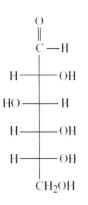

C.

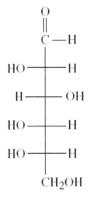

D.

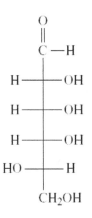

E. None of these is a diastereomer.

12. What is the product formed when the following monosaccharide is treated with Benedict's reagent?

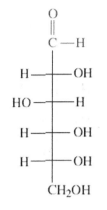

A.

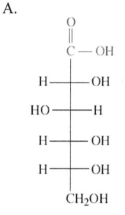

B.

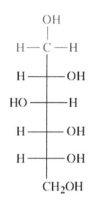

C.

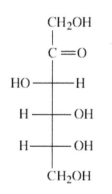

D. The given monosaccharide is a nonreducing sugar.

13. The following compound would be designated as _____.

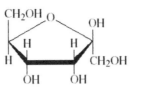

A. pyranose
B. furanose
C. nonreducing sugar
D. both A and C
E. both B and C

14. Which of the following would be designated as an α anomer?
A.

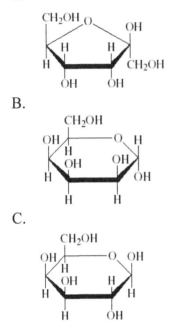

B.

C.

D. All are β anomers.

15. Consider the sweetness index given in the table.

TABLE 6.1 Relative Sweetness of Sugars and Artificial Sweeteners

Sweetener	Sweetness Relative to Sucrose (= 100)	Description
Simple Sugars		
Fructose	140–175	Fruit sugar, a monosaccharide that is a component of sucrose
Invert sugar (Hydrolyzed sucrose)	120	Found in honey
Sucrose	100	Table sugar, a disaccharide containing glucose and fructose
Xylitol	100	A sugar alcohol, used in sugar-free products
Glucose	75	Dextrose, the most common monosaccharide that is a component of sucrose and lactose
Erythritol	70	A sugar alcohol used in sugar-free products
Sorbitol	36–55	A sugar alcohol used in sugar-free products
Maltose	32	A disaccharide of glucose
Galactose	30	A monosaccharide that is a component of the disaccharide lactose
Lactose	15	Milk sugar, a disaccharide containing galactose and glucose

Which of the following would taste the sweetest?
A. 100% xylitol
B. a brand of maple syrup, 95% sucrose, 5% glucose
C. a brand of organic honey, 15% glucose, 85% invert sugar
D. 100% glucose

16. What is the correct ring structure for the α anomer in pyranose ring form for the following monosaccharide?

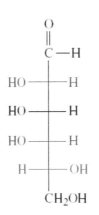

A.

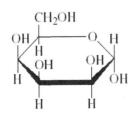

B.

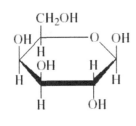

C.

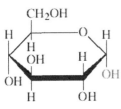

D.

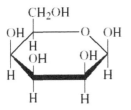

17. What will be the difference in the ring forms of the following two monosaccharides?

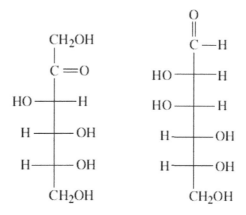

    A. the number of atoms in the ring
    B. the number of anomers possible
    C. the placement of the —OH on C1 relative to the ring (above versus below)
    D. the product being a reducing or nonreducing sugar

18. Which of the following is **not** a characteristic of fructose?
    A. also called fruit sugar
    B. a component of sucrose
    C. an epimer of glucose
    D. the sweetest monosaccharide

19. A monosaccharide is a component of both lactose and sucrose and is commonly known as blood sugar. This monosaccharide is _____.
    A. mannose
    B. galactose
    C. glucose
    D. ribose

20. Consider the following structure.

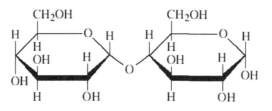

This structure represents _____.
    A. a nonreducing oligosaccharide
    B. a reducing disaccharide
    C. the product of a hydrolysis reaction
    D. both B and C

21. The following reaction symbolically represents a _____ .

A. hemiacetal reaction
B. dehydration reaction
C. condensation reaction
D. hydrolysis reaction

22. Which of the following does **not** contain a glycosidic bond?
A.

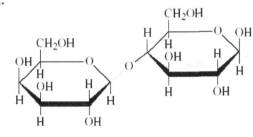

B.

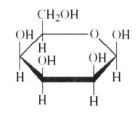

C.

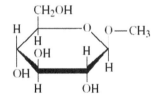

D. B and C
E. A, B, and C contain glycosidic bonds.

23. Determine the type of glycosidic bond in the following structure.

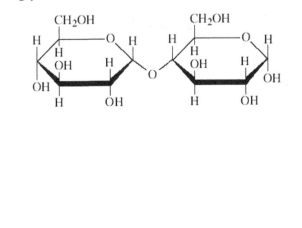

A. $\alpha(1\rightarrow4)$
B. $\beta(1\rightarrow4)$
C. $\alpha(1\rightarrow6)$
D. $\beta(1\rightarrow6)$

24. Which of the following describes sucrose?
    A. It is a reducing sugar.
    B. It undergoes hydrolysis to produce one type of monosaccharide.
    C. It is the most abundant disaccharide in nature.
    D. It is found in mammalian milk.
    E. All of the above describe sucrose.

25. The product(s) of the hydrolysis reaction of the following sugar would be:

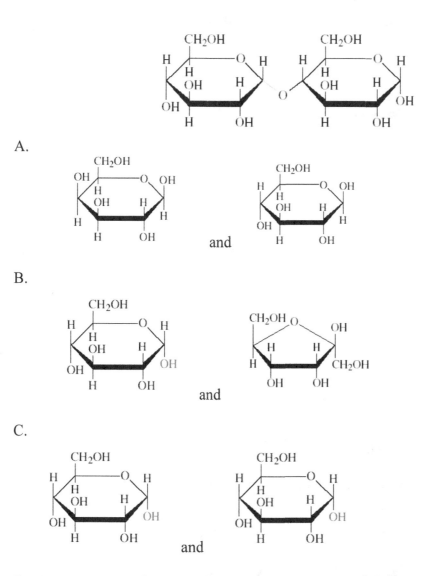

A.

B.

C.

D. Anomers cannot be determined from the given information.

26. Consider the segment of the following polysaccharide:

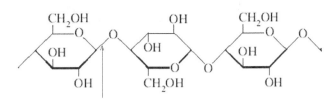

The arrow in the figure represents a(n) _____.
A. $\alpha(1\rightarrow4)$ bond
B. $\beta(1\rightarrow4)$ bond
C. $\alpha(1\rightarrow6)$ bond
D. $\beta(1\rightarrow6)$ bond

27. Which of the following is an example of a structural polysaccharide?
A. amylose
B. amylopectin
C. glycogen
D. chitin

28. Consider a storage polysaccharide that contains $\alpha(1\rightarrow4)$ bonds, is found in starch, and has branches about every 25 glucose units. This polysaccharide is _____.
A. amylose
B. amylopectin
C. glycogen
D. cellulose

29. Type O blood is available for transfusion. Recipients with the following blood types need a transfusion. Which can receive type O blood?
A. A
B. B
C. AB
D. A, B, and AB
E. Only recipients with type O blood would be compatible.

30. Consider the following, which represents the "backbone" of the blood type groups.

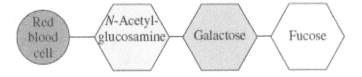

Groups bonded to which unit of the backbone distinguish the various blood types?
A. red blood cell
B. N-acetylglucosamine
C. galactose
D. fucose

Answers

1. C 2. C 3. B 4. A 5. C 6. E 7. B 8. C 9. D 10. A
11. E 12. A 13. B 14. B 15. C 16. A 17. A 18. C 19. C 20. B
21. D 22. B 23. A 24. C 25. C 26. B 27. D 28. B 29. D 30. C

Chapter 6 – Solutions to Odd-Numbered Problems

Practice Problems

6.1   a. polysaccharide   b. oligosaccharide   c. disaccharide

6.3   a. soluble   b. soluble   c. insoluble

6.5   a. secondary   b. primary   c. tertiary   d. secondary

6.7   a. ketone   b. ketone   c. aldehyde

6.9   a. D-isomer   b. L-isomer   c. D-isomer

6.11

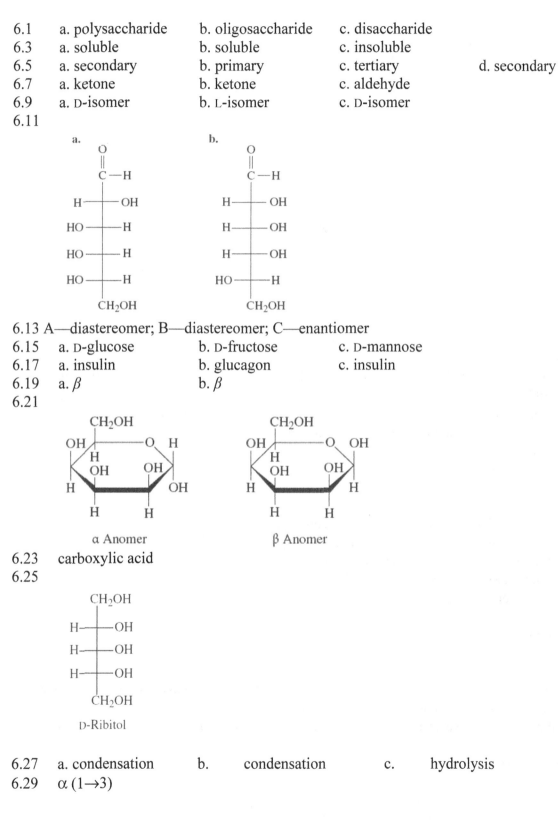

6.13 A—diastereomer; B—diastereomer; C—enantiomer

6.15   a. D-glucose   b. D-fructose   c. D-mannose

6.17   a. insulin   b. glucagon   c. insulin

6.19   a. β b. β

6.21

6.23   carboxylic acid

6.25

6.27   a. condensation   b.   condensation   c.   hydrolysis

6.29 $\alpha\,(1\rightarrow3)$

6.31

a. bond is $\beta(1 \rightarrow 4)$

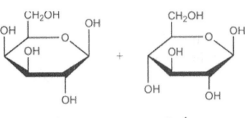

D-galactose   D-glucose

b. bond is $\alpha(1 \rightarrow 4)$

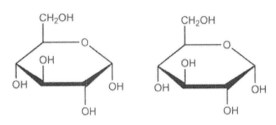

Both monosaccharides are D-glucose

6.33   a. sucrose   b. lactose   c. maltose   d. lactose

6.35   agave syrup

6.37   a. Both contain $\alpha(1 \rightarrow 4)$ glycosidic bonds and only D-glucose. Amylopectin also contains branching $\alpha(1 \rightarrow 6)$.
     b. Both contain $\alpha(1 \rightarrow 4)$ glycosidic bonds and branching $\alpha(1 \rightarrow 6)$ and only D-glucose. Branching occurs more often in glycogen than in amylopectin.

6.39   a. cellulose, chitin
     b. amylose, amylopectin
     c. amylose
     d. glycogen

6.41   a. No. A person with type B blood can only receive type B or O blood.
     b. No. A person with type B blood can only receive type B or O blood.

6.43   In contrast to the glucose polysaccharides, which contain only glucose as the repeating unit, heparin contains two monosaccharides as the repeating unit. The monosaccharides in heparin are also charged, whereas glucose is not.

Additional Problems

6.45 $C_4H_8O_4$

6.47   An oligosaccharide is smaller, containing between three and nine monosaccharide units, whereas a polysaccharide contains 10 or more monosaccharide units.

6.49   Soluble fibers mix with water and form a gel-like substance that gives a feeling of fullness when eaten.

6.51   aldehyde, hydroxyls (alcohol)

6.53   a. secondary   b. primary   c. secondary
     d. primary   e. secondary

6.55   Carbons 2–5 in glucose are secondary, C6 is primary.

6.57   a. enantiomer: left molecule is L-isomer, right molecule is D-isomer
       b. epimer, both are D
6.69   a. alpha   b. beta
6.61

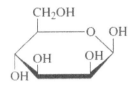

α-D-Mannose   β-D-Mannose

6.63

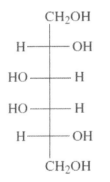

Galactose oxidized at C1

6.65

Galactose reduced at C1

6.67   a. yes   b. yes   c. no   d. no
6.69

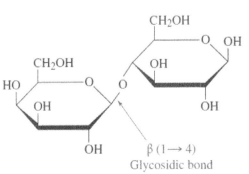

β (1 → 4)
Glycosidic bond

6.71

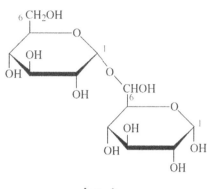

Isomaltose

6.73   a. sucrose   b. glucose   c. ʟ-fucose   d. amylose, amylopectin
       e. chitin
6.75   a. no   b. no

Challenge Problems

6.77

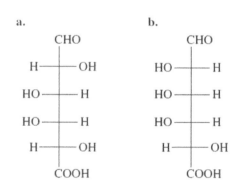

6.79

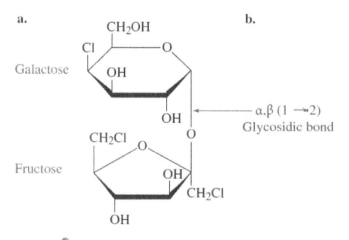

c. Splenda® is not a reducing sugar.

6.81   200 Calories; 9%

What's the Attraction?
Gas Laws, State Changes,
Solubility, and Lipids

7.1   Types of Attractive Forces

Learning Objectives
Upon completion of this material, a student should be able to do the following:
   A. Define the following key terms:

attractive force	**dipole–dipole attraction**
intermolecular force	**hydrogen bonding**
London forces	**ion–dipole attraction**
induced dipole	**ionic attraction**
permanent dipole	**salt**

   B. Describe five types of attractive forces present in compounds.
   C. Determine the type of intermolecular force from its chemical structure.

7.2   Gases: Attractive Forces Are Limited

Learning Objectives
Upon completion of this material, a student should be able to do the following:
   A. Define the following key terms:

pressure	**millimeters of mercury (mmHg)**
pounds per square inch (psi)	

   B. Define pressure.
   C. Convert pressure units.
   D. Apply and solve problems using Boyle's law.
   E. Apply and solve problems using Charles's law.
   F. Apply and solve problems using Gay-Lussac's law.
   G. Apply and solve problems using the combined gas law.
   F. Apply and solve problems using the ideal gas law.

7.3   Liquids and Solids: Attractive Forces Are Everywhere

Learning Objectives

Upon completion of this material, a student should be able to do the following:
   A. Define the following key terms:

changes of state	**deposition**
freezing	**physical equilibrium**
melting	**vapor pressure**
vaporization	**boiling**
condensation	**boiling point**
sublimation	**melting point**

   B. Describe the changes in the states of matter.
   C. Predict boiling points for liquids based on the attractive forces present.
   D. Predict relative vapor pressures for liquids based on the attractive forces present.

7.4   Attractive Forces and Solubility

Learning Objectives

Upon completion of this material, a student should be able to do the following:
   A. Define the following key terms:

solubility	**amphipathic**
golden rule of solubility	**hydrophobic**
triglycerides	**hydrophilic**
esterification	**micelle**
hydration	**emulsifier**

   B. State the golden rule of solubility.
   C. Predict the solubility of a molecule in water.
   D. Recognize an amphipathic molecule.
   E. Define the role of an emulsifier.
   F. Draw a fatty acid micelle using a cartoon representation.

7.5   Dietary Lipids

Learning Objectives

Upon completion of this material, a student should be able to do the following:
   A. Define the following key terms:

fat	**oil**

   B. Distinguish a fat from an oil.
   C. Describe the differences in melting points of fats and oils based on their attractive forces.
   D. Draw a triglyceride.

7.6   Attractive Forces and the Cell Membrane

Learning Objectives

Upon completion of this material, a student should be able to do the following:
   A. Define the following key terms:

phospholipids	**steroids**
fluid mosaic model	

   B. Draw a phospholipid bilayer.
   C. Locate the polar and nonpolar regions of a phospholipid and cholesterol.
   D. Describe the structure of a cell membrane.

Practice Test for Chapter 7

1. The type of intermolecular force depicted by the arrow in the image is _____.

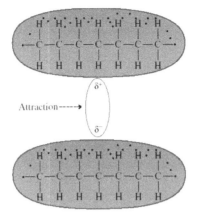

   A. London force
   B. dipole–dipole attraction
   C. hydrogen bonding
   D. ion–dipole attraction

2. What type(s) of intermolecular attraction would exist between molecules of the following type?

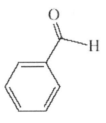

   A. London force
   B. dipole–dipole attraction
   C. hydrogen bonding
   D. A and B
   E. A, B, and C

3. How many hydrogen bonds could the following molecule form with water?

$$CH_3CHCH_2CH_3$$
$$|$$
$$OH$$

   A. none
   B. 1
   C. 2
   D. 3
   E. 4

4. Identify the strongest attractive force that could exist between the following pair of molecules.

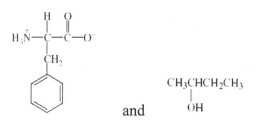

and   CH₃CHCH₂CH₃
              |
              OH

A. London force
B. dipole–dipole attraction
C. hydrogen bonding
D. ion–dipole attraction.

5. Convert a pressure of 37 psi to mmHg.
A. 37 mmHg
B. 2.5 mmHg
C. 1.9×10^3 mmHg
D. 0.049 mmHg

6. Consider a weather balloon that is filled at sea level where atmospheric pressure is about 760 mmHg and the temperature is 23 °C. This balloon is then transported to the top of a mountain to be released where the pressure is 680 mmHg and the temperature is 15 °C. Which of the following correctly describes how the volume of the balloon will change?
A. The volume will increase due to the pressure change and increase due to the temperature change.
B. The volume will decrease due to the pressure change and decrease due to the temperature change.
C. The volume will increase due to the pressure change and decrease due to the temperature change.
D. The volume will decrease due to the pressure change and increase due to the temperature change.

7. The lung capacity of an adult male diver is 5.40 L at a room pressure of 755 mmHg. If the diver's lung capacity is reduced to 4.90 L during a dive, what is the pressure in mmHg experienced by the diver?
A. 832 mmHg
B. 685 mmHg
C. 731 mmHg
D. 907 mmHg

8. The 275 mL sample of nitrogen gas is trapped in a container that has a flexible volume at 10.5 °C. What is the temperature of the sample when the volume of the gas is 395 mL? Assume that only the temperature changes.
A. 15.1 K
B. 407 K
C. 197 K
D. 7.31 K

9. A 22-L spun steel gas cylinder has an internal pressure of 6.75 atm at 25 °C. What will the internal pressure in this cylinder be at 37 °C?
   A. 9.99 atm
   B. 7.02 atm
   C. 6.49 atm
   D. 6.75 atm

10. A rubber ball has a volume of 5.00 L at 17 °C and 1.00 atm. If the pressure is changed to 2.00 atm and the temperature to 34 °C, what will be the new volume of this ball?
   A. 5.00 L
   B. 2.37 L
   C. 10. L
   D. 2.65 L

11. Which of the following substances would have the lowest vapor pressure at 25 °C?
   A. $CH_3CH_2CH_2CH_2CH_2CH_3$
   B. $CH_3CH_2CH_2$ $CH_2CH_2CH_2CH_3$
   C. $CH_3CH_2CH_2$ $CH_2CH_2CH_2$ $CH_2CH_2CH_3$
   D. $CH_3CH_2CH_2CH_2$ $CH_2CH_2CH_2$ $CH_2CH_2CH_2CH_2CH_3$

12. Which of the following substances would have the lowest boiling point?
   A.

   B.

   C.

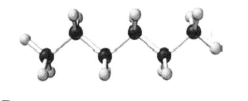

   D.

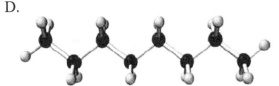

13. Compare the boiling points of the following substances. In which of the pairs of substances would the compound listed on the **left** have the **higher** boiling point?
    A. $CH_3CH_2CH_2CH_3$ and $CH_3CH_2CH_2OH$
    B. $CH_3CH_2CH_2CH_3$ and $CH_3CH_2NHCH_2CH_3$
    C. $CH_3CH_2CH_2CH_3$ and $CH_3CH_2CH_3$
    D. $CH_3CH_2CH_2CH_3$ and $CH_3CH_2OCH_2CH_3$

14. Which of the following does not characterize both boiling and melting?
    A. Heat must be added.
    B. A phase transition is involved
    C. The liquid state of matter is involved.
    D. All characterize melting and boiling.

15. Which of the following is a correct description of the manner in which the following molecule would interact with water?

    A. This molecule would be a hydrogen bond donor and water a hydrogen bond acceptor.
    B. This molecule would be a hydrogen bond acceptor and water a hydrogen bond donor.
    C. Both this molecule and water function as hydrogen bond acceptors and donors.
    D. This molecule would not hydrogen bond with water.

16. Which of the following pairs of compounds would most likely **not** be soluble in each other?
    A. NH_3 and CH_3OH
    B. $CH_3CH_2CH_2CH_3$ and $CH_3CH_2CH_2OCH_2CH_3$
    C. NH_4NO_3 and $CH_3CH_2OCH_2CH_3$
    D. $CH_3CH_2CH_2OH$ and $CH_3CH_2NH_2$

17. Compare the solubility of the following substances in water. In which of the pairs of substances would the compound listed on the **left** probably be **more soluble** in water?
    A. $CH_3CH_2CH_2OH$ and CH_3OH
    B. $CH_3CH_2CH_2OCH_2CH_3$ and $CH_3CH_2NH_2$
    C. KCl and CO_2
    D. $CH_3CH_2CH_3$ and $CH_3CH_2CH_2CH_2NH_2$

18. The "like" in the expression "like dissolves like" refers to molecular _____.
    A. polarity
    B. size
    C. shape
    D. all of the above

19. Consider the structure of a soap. Which of the following statements is(are) true?
    A. Soaps are amphipathic compounds.
    B. A soap contains a hydrophobic head.
    C. A soap contains a hydrophilic tail.
    D. All of the above statements are true.

20. A soap is able to dissolve nonpolar grease and oil in water by _____.
    A. forming a micelle around the oil with the soap tails in the interior
    B. forming a micelle around the oil with the soap heads in the interior
    C. forming an ion–dipole attraction to the oil
    D. surrounding the oil with carboxylate group of the soap

21. In a micelle formed from water and a soap, _____.
    A. hydrophobic heads are oriented toward the surface of the micelle
    B. hydrophobic tails are oriented toward the surface of the micelle
    C. hydrophilic heads are oriented toward the surface of the micelle
    D. hydrophilic tails are oriented toward the surface of the micelle

22. In "dry" cleaning, an oil stain can be removed by dissolving the oil directly in the liquid being used. Which of the following might make a dry cleaning liquid?
    A. CH_3CH_2OH
    B. $CH_3CH_2CH_2CH_2CH_2CH_3$
    C. $HOCH_2CH_2CH_2CH_2OH$
    D. All would be equally good candidates.

23. When glycerol and a fatty acid react, the reaction is called a(n) _____.
    A. esterification reaction
    B. condensation reaction
    C. hydrogenation reaction
    D. esterification or condensation reaction
    E. triglyceride reaction

24. Consider the bond formed when a triglyceride is produced. Which of the following general bonding schemes has the same type of bond enclosed in the circle?
    A.

    $$\begin{array}{c} O \\ \parallel \\ R-C-OR \end{array}$$

    ester
    B.

    $$\begin{array}{c} O \\ \parallel \\ R-C-O^- \end{array}$$

    carboxylate
    C.

    R—O—R   ether
    D.

    $$\begin{array}{c} O \\ \parallel \\ R-C-H \end{array}$$

    aldehyde

25. The following molecule was formed from the reaction of _____.

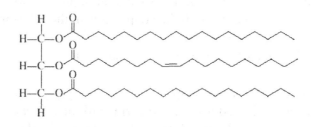

  A. glycerol and one saturated fatty acid and one unsaturated fatty acid
  B. glycerol and two different saturated fatty acids and one unsaturated fatty acid
  C. glycerol and one saturated fatty acid and two different unsaturated fatty acids
  D. glycerol and three different saturated fatty acids

26. Fats _____.
  A. contain mostly unsaturated fatty acids
  B. are carboxylate ions of carboxylic acids
  C. are liquids at room temperature
  D. have melting points near body temperature

27. The following is a cartoon of a soap molecule.

  Water would be the most strongly attracted to _____.
  A. the upper charged end
  B. the lower tail
  C. either end
  D. Water is not attracted to the molecule.

28. The primary structural components of cell membranes are _____.
  A. fatty acids
  B. triglycerides
  C. phospholipids
  D. cholesterol

29. If the following represents a phospholipid,

phospholipids might be arranged **between** the layers of the cell membrane as:
A.

B.

C.

D. The order of orientation is random.

30. Which of the following modulates the flexibility of a cell membrane?
A. phospholipids
B. cholesterol
C. proteins
D. triglycerides

Answers

1. A 2. D 3. D 4. D 5. C 6. C 7. A 8. B 9. B 10. D
11. D 12. B 13. C 14. D 15. B 16. B C17. C 18. A 19. A 20. A
21. C 22. B 23. D 24. A 25. A 26. D 27. A 28. C 29. C 30. B

Chapter 7 – Solutions to Odd-Numbered Problems

Practice Problems

7.1 Covalent bonds involve the sharing of electrons between atoms within a molecule, creating a chemical bond. Attractive forces involve attractions between positive and negative areas of different molecules. In attractive forces, electrons are not actually shared between atoms as in a chemical bond.

7.3 The dipole in London forces is temporary; the dipole in dipole–dipole forces is permanent.

7.5 A hydrogen bond acceptor is a pair of electrons on an O, N, or F.

7.7 The cation and anion of the ionic compound become hydrated as water molecules surround the ions breaking them apart. The partial negative end of water (the O) is attracted to the cation, while the partial positive end of water (the H) is attracted to the anion.

7.9 a. ionic attractions   b. London forces
     c. hydrogen bonding   d. dipole–dipole

7.11 Three hydrogen bonds can be formed.

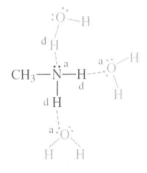

7.13 17 L

7.15 0.53 L

7.17 a. It would look like balloon C.
     b. It would look like balloon A.
     c. It would look like balloon C.
     d. It would look like balloon B.

7.19 The pressure decreases.

7.21 102 mL

7.23 Because moles of gas, volume, and temperature are the same in each tank, the pressures will be the same in each tank according to the ideal gas law.

7.25 The highest boiling point is found in the compound with the strongest attractive forces (hydrogen bonding), CH_3OH. The lowest boiling point is found in the compound with the weakest attractive forces (London force), CH_4. CH_3F is polar and will experience dipole–dipole attractions between its molecules, placing it between CH_3OH and CH_4 for the boiling point.

7.27 The alcohol molecule on the right has the highest boiling point because it has the strongest attractive forces present. It is an alcohol and has hydrogen bonding and dipole–dipole attractions. Of the two alkanes, the one with the greater amount of branching has the lower boiling point because of its decreased surface area.

7.29 Sevoflurane

7.31 a. insoluble   b. soluble   c. forms a micelle

7.33   a. The fatty acid salt is more soluble in water. The salt can form stronger ion−dipole interactions not available to the fatty acid.
        b. KCl. The ions in KCl readily dissolve in water through strong ion−dipole interactions, while $(CH_3)_3N$ interacts with water via weaker dipole−dipole interactions.

7.35   Even though fats and oils are both triglycerides, the large number of cis double bonds in oils lessens the number of attractive forces between the unsaturated hydrocarbon tails versus the saturated tails of the fats. More attractions means the tails pack more tightly, more like a solid, forming a fat.

7.37   The melting points are lower for the oils because it takes less energy (as heat) to move the loosely packed tails of an oil than it does the more tightly packed tails of a fat.

7.39   A triglyceride is a dietary lipid containing three fatty acids bonded to a glycerol molecule.

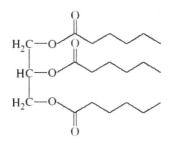

7.41   Phospholipids will form two layers called a bilayer, with the nonpolar tails of the two layers facing each other and their polar heads facing the water.

Additional Problems

7.43   Both are attractive forces that occur between positive and negative areas. A dipole−dipole attraction occurs between two opposite partial charges. An ion−dipole attraction occurs between opposite ionic charges and partial charges.

7.45

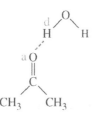

        The molecules can form more than one hydrogen bond. Acetone can form two hydrogen bonds, acting as an acceptor twice (two lone pairs on oxygen).

7.47   a. ionic attraction
        b. London forces
        c. London forces, dipole−dipole attractions, hydrogen bonding
        d. London forces
        e. London forces, dipole−dipole attractions
        f. London forces, dipole−dipole attractions, hydrogen bonding

7.49   3.00 atm

7.51   2 cc

7.53   12 L

7.55   10.7 L

7.57   535 °C

7.59   28.9 psi

7.61   No, you would only breathe in 0.98 L of He at this temperature and pressure.

7.63   An emulsifier can attract both a nonpolar and a polar substance, allowing both substances to be suspended in a mixture.

7.65   a. fatty acid   b. fat   c. CS$_2$ d. CH$_3$CH$_2$CH$_2$CH$_2$CH$_2$CH$_3$

7.67   The stain must be hydrophobic because it is not soluble in water.

7.69   Highest to lowest boiling point: a> c> b> d.
        a. five possible H-bonds per molecule (strongest)
        b. polar molecule
        c. three possible H-bonds per molecule
        d. nonpolar molecule (weakest)

7.71   Because the hydrocarbon chain is longer in octane (meaning the molecule has a greater surface area), the London forces between molecules are stronger, which makes the boiling point higher for octane.

7.73   A branched alkane has less surface contact with neighboring molecules than does a straight-chain alkane. The attractive forces are therefore stronger between the straight-chain alkane molecules, raising the boiling point and lowering the vapor pressure.

7.75   Niacin. The niacin overall contains more polar groups versus nonpolar areas than the vitamin A.

7.77   The soybean oil has more unsaturated fatty acids because it has a lower melting point.

7.79   The phospholipid head group contains many more atoms than the three atoms in the carboxylate head group of a soap.

7.81   Cell membranes contain cholesterol inserted into the phospholipid layer, carbohydrates on the outer surface, and proteins that span the membrane or sit on either surface of the membrane.

Challenge Problems

7.83   1900 L

7.85   Phospholipids are amphipathic molecules. They act to emulsify the nonpolar oil and the polar water in the mayonnaise, forming a thick mixture.

7.87

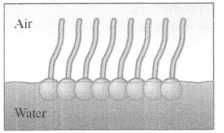

Hydrocarbons would interact with nonpolar air, polar heads with water at surface.

7.89   a. Honey
        b. Hydrogen bonding, dipole–dipole attractions, and London forces. A glucose in ring form can make many more hydrogen bonds to itself than water molecules can make to itself.
        c. Because there are so many more hydrogen bonds possible between sugar molecules in honey, the honey is more viscous than water.
        d. By adding soap to the water, the hydrogen bonding network between the water molecules is disrupted, and the paper clip can no longer float on the surface.

Chapter 8

Solution Chemistry: How Sweet Is Your Tea?

8.1   Solutions Are Mixtures

Learning Objectives

Upon completion of this material, a student should be able to do the following:
   A. Define the following key terms:

solution	**aqueous solution**
solute	**colloid**
solvent	**suspension**

   B. Distinguish solute and solvent.
   C. Identify solutions, colloids, and suspensions.

8.2   Formation of Solutions

Learning Objectives

Upon completion of this material, a student should be able to do the following:
   A. Define the following key terms:

solvation	**saturated solution**
hydration	**Henry's law**
unsaturated solution	

   B. Define saturated and dilute solutions.
   C. Predict the effect of temperature on the solubility of a solute.
   D. Predict the effect of pressure on the solubility of a gas in a liquid.

8.3   Chemical Equations for Solution Formation

Learning Objectives

Upon completion of this material, a student should be able to do the following:
   A. Define the following key terms:

electrolyte	**weak electrolyte**
strong electrolyte	**law of conservation of matter**
ionize	**equivalent (Eq)**
nonelectrolyte	

   B. Predict if different types of electrolytes will fully, partially, or not dissociate when dissolved in a solution.
   C. Write chemical equations for hydration of electrolytes, nonelectrolytes, and weak electrolytes.
   D. Calculate the number of milliequivalents present for an ionic compound that fully dissociates in solution.
   E. Convert from mEq to moles.

8.4   Concentration

Learning Objectives
Upon completion of this material, a student should be able to do the following:
- A. Define the following key terms:

  concentration   **molarity**
- B. Express concentration in molarity units.
- C. Express concentration in percent units.
- D. Express concentration in parts per million and parts per billion.

8.5   Dilution

Learning Objectives
Upon completion of this material, a student should be able to do the following:
- A. Calculate concentrations or determine volumes using the dilution equation.
- B. Calculate initial volumes of concentrated stock solutions from a dilution factor.

8.6   Osmosis and Diffusion

Learning Objectives
Upon completion of this material, a student should be able to do the following:
- A. Define the following key terms:

  semipermeable membrane   **hypertonic solution**
  isotonic solution   **crenation**
  hypotonic solution   **physiological solution**
  osmosis   **diffusion**
  osmotic pressure   **dialysis**
- B. Predict the direction of osmosis or diffusion given the concentration on both sides of a semipermeable membrane.

8.7   Transport Across Cell Membranes

Learning Objectives
Upon completion of this material, a student should be able to do the following:
- A. Define the following key terms:

  passive diffusion   **active transport**
  facilitated transport
- B. Characterize three forms of transport across a cell membrane.

1. In which of the following would ethanol be classified the solvent?
   A. 35 mL of ethanol is mixed with 65 mL of methanol.
   B. 100 mL of ethanol is mixed with enough water to form 115 mL of solution.
   C. 35 g of ethanol is mixed with enough isopropyl alcohol to produce 150 g of solution.
   D. Ethanol is not the solvent in any of the solutions described.

2. Honey is mixed in hot tea. The resulting combination of honey and hot tea would be classified as
   a _____.
   A. suspension
   B. colloid
   C. solution
   D. solvent

3. Blood is a _____ of plasma and blood cells that can be separated by
   centrifugation.
   A. suspension
   B. colloid
   C. solution
   D. None of the above correctly classifies blood.

4. What happens to the solubility of oxygen in blood when a person drives from Kona, Hawaii, at
   sea level to the top of Mauna Kea at an almost 14,000-foot elevation?
   A. It decreases.
   B. It increases.
   C. It remains constant.
   D. Solubility cannot be predicted from the information given.

5. Consider two identical bottles of soft drink. One is stored in the refrigerator and one is stored at
   room temperature. When opened, which one will release more gas **from the liquid**?
   A. the one stored at room temperature
   B. the one stored in the refrigerator
   C. neither; they will release the same amount of gas regardless of temperature.
   D. cannot be predicted based on the given information.

6. The following picture was taken after table salt was added to water after the mixture was thoroughly stirred for 5 minutes. The pictured mixture probably represents a(n) _____.

A. heterogeneous mixture
B. saturated solution
C. equilibrium state
D. all of the above

7. Consider the following image of containers of the same carbonated beverage: a capped 2 L bottle, an open 250 ml beaker, and a closed 12 oz can.

In which container is the pressure of CO_2 likely to be the smallest?
A. 2 L bottle
B. 250 mL beaker
C. 12 oz can
D. either the 2 L bottle or the 12 oz can
E. It is impossible to predict.

8. For **both** solid and gaseous solutes, which of the following is true?
A. Solubility increases with increasing temperature.
B. Solubility decreases with increasing temperature.
C. Solubility increases with increasing pressure.
D. Solubility decreases with increasing pressure.
E. None of the above is true for both solid and gaseous solutes.

9. Which of the following is most likely to be a weak electrolyte?
A. $C_6H_{12}O_6(s)$
B. $NH_4NO_3(s)$
C. $CH_3COOH(l)$
D. $CH_3OH(l)$

10. When HF(*l*) dissolves in water, the following reaction occurs. HF is classified as _____.

$$HF(l) \underset{H_2O}{\rightleftharpoons} H^+(aq) + F^-(aq)$$

    A. a weak electrolyte
    B. a nonelectrolyte
    C. a strong electrolyte
    D. The reaction alone cannot be used to predict.

11. The following reaction indicates _____.

$$MgCl_2(s) \xrightarrow{H_2O} Mg^{2+}(aq) + 2\,Cl^-(aq)$$

    A. that the solubility of the solute will decrease as the temperature is increased.
    B. that the solute is a weak electrolyte.
    C. that the reaction is a hydration.
    D. all of the above

12. The balanced equation for the hydration of $AlCl_3$ would contain how many total ions or molecules in the products?
    A. 1
    B. 2
    C. 3
    D. 4
    E. 5

13. The products of the correctly balanced equation for the hydration of $BaCl_2$ would be _____.
    A. $Ba^{2+}(aq) + Cl_2^{2-}(aq)$.
    B. $Ba^{2+}(aq) + 2Cl^-(aq)$.
    C. $BaCl_2(aq)$.
    D. $Ba^{1+}(aq) + 2Cl^-(aq)$.

14. Which of the following concentration units is used to represent the amount of electrolytes in body fluid?
    A. M
    B. %(m/v)
    C. %(m/m)
    D. mEq/L

15. Which of the following conversion factors could be used to represent the relationship between equivalents and moles of PO_4^{3-}?

A. $\dfrac{1\,Eq\,PO_4^{3-}}{1\,mol\,PO_4^{3-}}$

B. $\dfrac{1\,Eq\,PO_4^{3-}}{3\,mol\,PO_4^{3-}}$

C. $\dfrac{3\,Eq\,PO_4^{3-}}{1\,mol\,PO_4^{3-}}$

D. $\dfrac{3\,Eq\,PO_4^{3-}}{3\,mol\,PO_4^{3-}}$

16. How many equivalents of CO_3^{2-} are present in a solution that contains 0.750 mole of CO_3^{2-}?
    A. 1.50 Eq
    B. 0.750 Eq
    C. 0.250 Eq
    D. 2.25 Eq

17. How many mmol of Ca^{2+} are present in a solution that contains 2.30 mEq of Ca^{2+}?
    A. 2.30 mmol
    B. 4.60 mmol
    C. 1.15 mmol
    D. 6.90 mmol

18. A Ringer's solution for intravenous fluid replacement typically has a concentration of 77.5 mEq Cl^- per 0.500 L of solution. If a patient receives 0.750 L of Ringer's solution, how many equivalents of Cl^- were given?
    A. 116 Eq
    B. 0.116 Eq
    C. 51. 7 Eq
    D. 0.0775 Eq

19. What is the molarity of a solution prepared by dissolving 2.50 moles of NaCl in enough water to produce 3.00 L solution?
    A. 0.833 M
    B. 2.50 M
    C. 7.50 M
    D. 1.20 M

20. How many moles of KCl are present in 574 mL of a 0.660 M KCl solution?
    A. 0.660 mol
    B. 379 mol
    C. 1.15 mol
    D. 0.379 mol

21. What is the molarity of a solution prepared by dissolving 50.0 g of KCl in enough water to yield 1.50 L of solution?
   A. 33.3 M
   B. 0.0300 M
   C. 0.447 M
   D. 0.671 M

22. Calculate the concentration in %(m/m) for a solution prepared by dissolving 58.5 g of Na_2SO_4 in 200.0 g of distilled water.
   A. 22.6%
   B. 29.2%
   C. 3.41%
   D. 11.7%

23. 0.125 L of a 55.0 mg/mL hydrocortisone solution is needed. What volume of a 210.0 mg/ml solution should be diluted to obtain this solution?
   A. 32.7 mL
   B. 477 mL
   C. 0.0327 mL
   D. 6.88 mL
   E. 26.2 mL

24. How many grams of glucose would be needed to prepare 2.00 L of a 5.10% (m/v) solution?
   A. 10.2 g
   B. 102 g
   C. 2.55 g
   D. 25.5 g

25. How many liters of a 5.00% (m/v) solution of NaCl can be prepared from 575 mL of a stock 12.5% (m/v) solution?
   A. 230 L
   B. 1440 L
   C. 0.230 L
   D. 1.44 L

26. A pharmacist needs to prepare 450 mL of a 1X solution for a patient. How much 150X solution will be needed?
   A. 450 mL
   B. 3.0 mL
   C. 0.33 mL
   D. 6.75 mL

27. In which of the following processes is the direction of ion or molecule movement opposite to that which will equalize concentrations?
    A. osmosis
    B. diffusion
    C. active transport
    D. passive diffusion
    E. none of these

28. Consider the following image, which depicts a cell in a solution.

Based on the effect on the cell, the solution would be classified as _____.
    A. hypertonic, and the water is flowing out of the cell
    B. hypotonic, and the water is flowing into the cell
    C. hypertonic, and the water is flowing into the cell
    D. hypotonic, and the water is flowing out of the cell
    E. isotonic, and there is no net water flow

29. Consider the diagram showing methods of transport across a cell membrane.

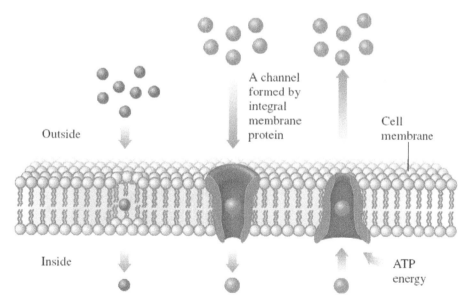

A Na^+ ion is to be transported across the membrane with an input of energy. Which method of transport will be used?
    A. passive diffusion
    B. facilitated transport
    C. active transport
    D. Not enough information is given to determine the method.

30. A red blood cell that is isotonic with 0.90% (m/v) NaCl and 5% (m/v) glucose will undergo _____.

    A. lysis if placed in distilled water.
    B. crenation if placed in a 1.90% (m/v) NaCl and 5% (m/v) glucose solution.
    C. no change if placed in a 0.90% (m/v) NaCl and 5% (m/v) glucose solution.
    D. all of the above

Answers

1. B   2. C   3. A   4. A   5. A   6. D   7. B   8. E   9. C   10. A
11. C   12. D   13. B   14. D   15. C   16. A   17. C   18. B   19. A   20. D
21. C   22. A   23. A   24. B   25. D   26. B   27. C   28. A   29. C   30. D

Chapter 8 – Solutions to Odd-Numbered Problems

Practice Problems

8.1   a. solute, oxygen; solvent, nitrogen
       b. solute, zinc; solvent, copper
       c. solute, blue food coloring; solvent, ethanol

8.3   a. colloid   b. solution   c. solution

8.5   a. no, not saturated   b. yes, saturated

8.7   a. increase   b. decrease   c. increase

8.9   a. Decreasing the temperature increases the solubility of the gas in the soda, so more of the gas stays in the solution, and capping the bottle increases the CO_2 pressure over the solution and increases the solubility of CO_2.
       b. If the lid is on tight, no gas can escape, and gas that escapes from the solution will build up a pressure above the solution. At some point, an equilibrium is reached in which no more gas will escape from the solution.
       c. The solubilities of most solid solutes decrease with lower temperature, so less sugar will dissolve in the iced tea.

8.11   At sea level since atmospheric pressure is higher at sea level.

8.13   a. fully dissociate   b. partially dissociate c. not dissociate

8.15   a. $KF(s) \xrightarrow{H_2O} K^+(aq) + F^-(aq)$

       b. $HCN(g) \underset{H_2O}{\rightleftharpoons} H^+(aq) + CN^-(aq)$

       c. $C_6H_{12}O_6(s) \xrightarrow{H_2O} C_6H_{12}O_6(aq)$

8.17   a. $CaCl_2(s) \xrightarrow{H_2O} Ca^{2+}(aq) + 2Cl^-(aq)$

       b. $NaOH(s) \xrightarrow{H_2O} Na^+(aq) + OH^-(aq)$

       c. $KBr(s) \xrightarrow{H_2O} K^+(aq) + Br^-(aq)$

       d. $Fe(NO_3)_3(s) \xrightarrow{H_2O} Fe^{3+}(aq) + 3NO_3^-(aq)$

8.19   4.25 Eq

8.21   0.0770 mole Na^+

8.23   1.25 mmoles $Ca2^+$/L

8.25   17 M

8.27   0.43 M

8.29   35.7 g of KBr

8.31   0.5% (m/v)

8.33   a. 5.00%   b. 6.3%

8.35   0.117 g insulin

8.37   5 ppm, 5000 ppb

8.39   6 L

8.41   3% (m/v)

8.43 Add 62.5 mL of the 0.90% NaCl stock solution to enough distilled water for a total volume of 250 mL of solution.

8.45 21 mL

8.47 a. leave   b. crenate   c. hypertonic

8.49 hypertonic, isotonic

8.51 a. hypertonic   b. hypotonic   c. hypertonic   d. isotonic

8.53 a. passive diffusion
     b. facilitated transport
     c. active transport
     d. facilitated transport

Additional Problems

8.55 Benzoin is the solute and ethanol is the solvent.

8.57 a. colloid   b. solution   c. colloid

8.59 a. decrease   b. increase   c. decrease

8.61 The person has less oxygen in the lungs, so less can move into the bloodstream and the concentration in the blood is therefore less.

8.63 a. fully dissociate   b. partially dissociate   c. not dissociate

8.65 a. $NaI(s) \xrightarrow{H_2O} Na^+(aq) + I^-(aq)$

    b.

$$\text{OH}(l) \underset{H_2O}{\rightleftharpoons} \text{O}^-(aq) + \text{H}^+(aq)$$

    c. $C_6H_{12}O_6(s) \xrightarrow{H_2O} C_6H_{12}O_6(aq)$

8.67 2.68 Eq Ca^{2+}

8.69 7 mEq Ca^{2+}

8.71 12.5 mmole/L

8.73 1.87 M

8.75 0.80 M

8.77 90. mL of ethanol

8.79 0.5% (m/v)

8.81 40 g dextrose

8.83 70–180 ppm urea nitrogen

8.85 a. 1.0 M HNO_3
     b. 0.75 M KOH

8.87 a. 0.90 L
     b. 1.25 L

8.89 Add 50 mL of the stock solution (18% (m/v) to enough water to make 1.0 L.

8.91 10X; 5%

8.93 5 mL

8.95 a. hypertonic
     b. hypotonic
     c. isotonic

8.97 The cells will attempt to dilute the higher than normal concentration of Na^+ in the tissues by moving more water into the tissues causing fluid retention.

8.99   If osmosis is water moving from a lower concentrated solution to a higher concentrated solution, balancing out the concentrations, the reverse would require water moving in the opposite direction. Less pure water (higher concentration of solutes) is forced (requires energy) through a filter (semipermeable membrane), removing more impurities, making water drinkable.

8.101   a. no   b. no   c. yes

Challenge Problems

8.103   According to Henry's law, more nitrogen would dissolve in the bloodstream at lower depths (higher pressure) than at the surface (lower pressure). When a diver ascends to the surface quickly, the pressure of the air in the tank (and therefore the air in the lungs) lessens more rapidly than a person can expel the nitrogen. Unable to stay dissolved in the bloodstream, nitrogen gas bubbles begin forming in the bloodstream, causing the condition.

8.105   Water will move from solution A to solution B because solution B is a higher concentrated solution (more solute/solution). It does not matter that the albumin particles are huge; osmotic flow depends on the concentration, not the size of the particles. Since solution B has a higher solute concentration, it exerts a higher osmotic pressure.

8.107   Yes. Add 144 mL from the stock vials to water for a total volume of 240 mL.

Acids, Bases, and Buffers in the Body

9.1 Acids and Bases—Definitions

Learning Objectives

Upon completion of this material, a student should be able to do the following:
  A. Define the following key terms:

acid	acidic
hydronium ion, H_3O^+	basic
base	

  B. Describe the physical characteristics of an acid and a base.
  C. Identify an acid and a base in a chemical equation using the Arrhenius or Brønsted-Lowry definition.

9.2 Strong Acids and Bases

Learning Objectives

Upon completion of this material, a student should be able to do the following:
  A. Define the following key terms:

strong acid	weak base
weak acid	salt
strong base	neutralization

  B. Name the six strong acids.
  C. Characterize strong bases.
  D. Compare a strong acid to a weak acid.
  E. Name acids from their anions and vice versa.
  F. Write and balance a neutralization reaction.

9.3 Chemical Equilibrium

Learning Objectives

Upon completion of this material, a student should be able to do the following:
  A. Define the following key terms:

chemical equilibrium	Le Châtelier's principle
equilibrium constant, K	

  B. Define chemical equilibrium.
  C. Write an equilibrium expression for K.
  D. Apply Le Châtelier's principle to chemical equilibrium.

9.4   Weak Acids and Bases

Learning Objectives

Upon completion of this material, a student should be able to do the following:
A. Define the following key terms:
    acid dissociation constant, K_a   **conjugate acid**
    conjugate base   **conjugate acid–base pair**
B. Apply the principles of chemical equilibrium to weak acids and bases.
C. Determine strengths of weak acids based on their K_a values.
D. Identify conjugate acid–base pairs.
E. Complete a chemical equation for a conjugate acid–base in water.

9.5   pH and the pH Scale

Learning Objectives

Upon completion of this material, a student should be able to do the following:
A. Define the following key terms:
    autoionization of water   **pH**
    neutral
B. Determine if a solution is acidic, basic, or neutral if given its pH or $[H_3O^+]$.
C. Calculate the pH if given the $[H_3O^+]$.
D. Calculate the $[H_3O^+]$ if given the pH.

9.6 pK_a

Learning Objectives

Upon completion of this material, a student should be able to do the following:
A. Define the following key term.
    pK_a
B. Predict the strength of a weak acid from its pK_a value.
C. Based on pH and pK_a values, predict whether acid or base predominates.

9.7   Amino Acids: Common Biological Weak Acids

Learning Objectives

Upon completion of this material, a student should be able to do the following:
A. Define the following key terms:
    amino acids   **isoelectric point (pI)**
    zwitterion
B. Apply the definition of isoelectric point to predict the charge of an amino acid at points below, at, and above the pI value.
C. Predict the relative amounts of neutral versus charged compounds present by comparing pK_a values.

9.8 Buffers and Blood: The Bicarbonate Buffer System

Learning Objectives

Upon completion of this material, a student should be able to do the following:

A. Define the following key terms:

    buffer   **hyperventilation**
    homeostasis   **respiratory alkalosis**
    hypoventilation   **metabolic acidosis**
    respiratory acidosis   **metabolic alkalosis**

B. Apply the properties of a buffer by predicting the direction in which the bicarbonate buffer equilibrium will shift with changes in ventilation rate.

Practice Test for Chapter 9

1. Which of the following describes a solution that would be classified as basic?
   A. contains a metal ion and hydroxide ion
   B. would have a sour taste
   C. could be capable of corroding a metal
   D. contains a species that can donate a proton or form H_3O^+ ion

2. For the following reaction:
   $$NH_3(aq) + H_3O^+(aq) \rightarrow H_2O(l) + NH_4^+(aq)$$
   which of the following is a correct statement?
   A. NH_3 is the acid and H_3O^+ is the base.
   B. NH_3 is the base and H_3O^+ is the acid.
   C. H_2O and H_3O^+ are both acids.
   D. NH_3 and NH_4^+ are both bases.

3. In which of the following reactions does water act as a proton donor?
   A. $HBr(aq) + H_2O(l) \rightarrow H_3O^+(aq) + Br^-(aq)$
   B. $H_2O(l) + CN^-(aq) \rightarrow HCN(aq) + OH^-(aq)$
   C. $HCl(g) + H_2O(l) \rightarrow H_3O^+(aq) + Cl^-(aq)$
   D. none of the above

4. Which of the following would be classified as a strong acid?
   A. HF
   B. HNO_2
   C. HCl
   D. H_3PO_4
   E. All of the above are strong acids.

5. Consider the bromate ion, BrO_3^-. What would be the name and formula for the acid formed from this ion?
   A. bromous acid, H_3BrO_3
   B. hydrobromic acid, $HBrO_3$
   C. bromic acid, $HBrO_3$
   D. bromic acid, HBr
   E. bromous acid, $HBrO_3$

6. Which of the following compounds will completely ionize in water?
   A. NH_3
   B. H_2CO_3
   C. CH_3COOH
   D. KOH

7. When the equation is balanced, the products of the following reaction are:
   $$H_2SO_4 + Ca(OH)_2 \rightarrow$$
   A. $CaSO_4 + 2\ H_2O$
   B. $CaSO_4 + H_2O$
   C. $SO_4(OH)_2 + CaH_2$
   D. $2SO_4OH + 2CaH$

8. What is the equilibrium constant expression for the following reaction?

$$CaCO_3(s) + 2 HI(aq) \rightleftharpoons CaI_2(aq) + CO_2(g) + H_2O(l)$$

A. $K = \dfrac{[CaI_2][CO_2][H_2O]}{[CaCO_3][HI]}$

B. $K = \dfrac{[CaI_2][CO_2][H_2O]}{[CaCO_3][HI]^2}$

C. $K = \dfrac{[CaI_2][CO_2]}{[HI]}$

D. $K = \dfrac{[CaI_2][CO_2]}{[HI]^2}$

9. At a certain temperature, K for the following reaction is 54.

$$H_2(g) + I_2(g) \rightleftharpoons 2HI(g)$$

This means at equilibrium, the _____.
A. products are present in greater amounts than the reactants
B. reactants are present in greater amounts than the products
C. products and reactants are present in equal amounts
D. amounts of reactants and products will vary depending on the starting amount of reactant

10. Consider the following reaction.

$$2 SO_2(g) + O_2(g) \rightleftharpoons 2 SO_3(g) + heat$$

Which of the following will increase the amount of SO_3?
A. increasing the temperature
B. removing O_2
C. adding SO_2
D. All increase the amount of SO_3.

11. Which of the following changes will increase the amount of product at equilibrium for an endothermic reaction?
A. removing the product as it forms
B. increasing the concentration of a reactant
C. increasing the temperature of the reaction
D. A and B
E. All of the above will increase the amount of product.

12. Based on the table given below, rank the following acids in order of increasing strength, weakest to strongest (left to right).

HCN   HCl   HNO$_2$ NH$_4^+$

TABLE 9.6 K_a Values for Substances Acting as Weak Acids (25 °C)		
Name	Formula	K_a
Hydrogen sulfate ion	HSO$_4^-$	1.0×10^{-2}
Phosphoric acid	H$_3$PO$_4$	7.5×10^{-3}
Hydrofluoric acid	HF	6.5×10^{-4}
Nitrous acid	HNO$_2$	4.5×10^{-4}
Formic acid	HCOOH	1.8×10^{-4}
Lactic acid	CH$_3$CH(OH)COOH	1.4×10^{-4}
Acetic acid	CH$_3$COOH	1.75×10^{-5}
Carbonic acid	H$_2$CO$_3$	4.5×10^{-7}
Dihydrogen phosphate ion	H$_2$PO$_4^-$	6.6×10^{-8}
Ammonium ion	NH$_4^+$	6.3×10^{-10}
Hydrocyanic acid	HCN	6.2×10^{-10}
Bicarbonate ion	HCO$_3^-$	4.8×10^{-11}
Hydrogen phosphate ion	HPO$_4^{2-}$	1.0×10^{-12}
Water	H$_2$O	1.8×10^{-16}

A. HCN < HNO$_2$ < NH$_4^+$< HCl
B. HCN < NH$_4^+$< HNO$_2$ < HCl
C. HCl< HNO$_2$< NH$_4^+$ < HCN
D. HCl ≈ HNO$_2$< NH$_4^+$ < HCN

13. What is the conjugate base of HCN in the following reaction?

$$H_2O(l) + CN^-(aq) \rightleftharpoons HCN(aq) + OH^-(aq)$$

A. H$_2$CN$^+$
B. OH$^-$
C. H$_2$O
D. CN$^-$

14. Which of the following is true of HCO$_3^-$?
A. CO$_3^{2-}$ is the conjugate base.
B. H$_2$CO$_3$ is the conjugate acid.
C. H$_2$O is the conjugate base.
D. H$_3$O$^+$ is the conjugate acid.
E. A and B

15. The products of the following reaction would be _____.

$$F^-(aq) + H_2O(l) \rightleftharpoons$$

A. $HF(aq) + H_3O^+(aq)$
B. $H_2F^+(aq) + OH^-(aq)$
C. $HF(aq) + OH^-(aq)$
D. $H_2F^+(aq) + H_3O^+(aq)$

16. What is the log of 1.75×10^{-3} and the inverse (INV or 10^x) log of -4.55, respectively?
A. $0.243, 3.54 \times 10^4$
B. $-2.76, 2.82 \times 10^{-5}$
C. $2.76, 2.82 \times 10^{-5}$
D. $3.24, 5.5 \times 10^{-4}$
E. -2.76. It is not possible to take the inverse log of a negative number.

17. A sample of seawater has a pH of 8.23. This solution is _____.
A. basic
B. acidic
C. neutral

18. A grapefruit has a $[H_3O^+]$ of 3.35×10^{-3}. This solution is _____.
A. basic
B. acidic
C. neutral

19. What is the pH of solution of coffee with $[H_3O^+]$ of 6.3×10^{-5}?
A. 9.67
B. -4.20
C. 1.30
D. 4.20

20. What is the $[H_3O^+]$ of a baking soda solution with a pH of 9.22?
A. 2.2×10^{-9}
B. 9.65×10^{-1}
C. 6.03×10^{-10}
D. 1.01×10^4

21. As the pK_a of an acid increases, the strength of the acid _____.
A. increases
B. decreases
C. remains constant

22. The pK_a of HF is 3.19. At a pH of 5.25, which of the following forms predominates?
A. HF
B. F^-
C. H_2F^+
D. HF and F would be present in the same amounts.

23. The pK_a of HCN is 9.12. If $[HCN] = [CN^-]$, the pH of the solution must be _____.
   A. 9.12
   B. > 9.12
   C. < 9.12
   D. between 7.00 and 9.12

24. Using the pK_a values given in the table below, which of the following has the strongest acid of the pair listed on the left?

TABLE 9.6 K_a Values for Substances Acting as Weak Acids (25 °C)		
Name	Formula	K_a
Hydrogen sulfate ion	HSO_4^-	1.0×10^{-2}
Phosphoric acid	H_3PO_4	7.5×10^{-3}
Hydrofluoric acid	HF	6.5×10^{-4}
Nitrous acid	HNO_2	4.5×10^{-4}
Formic acid	$HCOOH$	1.8×10^{-4}
Lactic acid	$CH_3CH(OH)COOH$	1.4×10^{-4}
Acetic acid	CH_3COOH	1.75×10^{-5}
Carbonic acid	H_2CO_3	4.5×10^{-7}
Dihydrogen phosphate ion	$H_2PO_4^-$	6.6×10^{-8}
Ammonium ion	NH_4^+	6.3×10^{-10}
Hydrocyanic acid	HCN	6.2×10^{-10}
Bicarbonate ion	HCO_3^-	4.8×10^{-11}
Hydrogen phosphate ion	HPO_4^{2-}	1.0×10^{-12}
Water	H_2O	1.8×10^{-16}

   A. HCO_3^- and H_2CO_3
   B. HPO_4^{2-} and $H_2PO_4^-$
   C. $H_2PO_4^-$ and H_3PO_4
   D. All pairs have the stronger acid listed on the right.

25. Using the pK_a values in the following table, predict the products of the following reaction.

$$HCO_3^- (aq) + H_2PO_4^- (aq) \rightleftharpoons$$

TABLE 9.6 K_a Values for Substances Acting as Weak Acids (25 °C)		
Name	Formula	K_a
Hydrogen sulfate ion	HSO_4^-	1.0×10^{-2}
Phosphoric acid	H_3PO_4	7.5×10^{-3}
Hydrofluoric acid	HF	6.5×10^{-4}
Nitrous acid	HNO_2	4.5×10^{-4}
Formic acid	HCOOH	1.8×10^{-4}
Lactic acid	$CH_3CH(OH)COOH$	1.4×10^{-4}
Acetic acid	CH_3COOH	1.75×10^{-5}
Carbonic acid	H_2CO_3	4.5×10^{-7}
Dihydrogen phosphate ion	$H_2PO_4^-$	6.6×10^{-8}
Ammonium ion	NH_4^+	6.3×10^{-10}
Hydrocyanic acid	HCN	6.2×10^{-10}
Bicarbonate ion	HCO_3^-	4.8×10^{-11}
Hydrogen phosphate ion	HPO_4^{2-}	1.0×10^{-12}
Water	H_2O	1.8×10^{-16}

A. $CO_3^{2-}(aq) + H_3PO_4(aq)$
B. $H_2CO_3(aq) + HPO_4^{2-}(aq)$
C. $H_2CO_3(aq) + PO_4^{3-}(aq)$
D. The products cannot be predicted.

26. Which of the following represents the zwitterion of the amino acid valine?

A.

B.

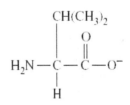

C.

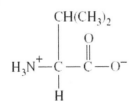

D. None of these represents the zwitterion.

27. The zwitterion structure for glycine is as follows. Glycine has a pI = 6.0.

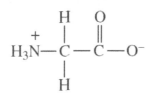

What will be the charge on glycine at physiological pH?
A. −1
B. +1
C. 0

28. Under what conditions would the following reaction occur?

A. addition of an acid
B. decrease in the pH
C. increase in the hydronium ion concentration
D. addition of a proton acceptor

29. Hyperventilation _____.
A. is also known as respiratory alkalosis
B. results in decreased amounts of CO_2 in the blood
C. increases the pH of the blood
D. upsets the bicarbonate balance of the blood
E. All of the above are characteristic of hyperventilation.

30. The blood buffer system can be represented as:

$$CO_2(g) + H_2O(l) \rightleftharpoons H_3O^+(aq) + HCO_3^-(aq)$$

Vomiting can cause a loss of the hydronium ion from blood. This causes_____.
A. metabolic alkalosis
B. a shift in the reaction toward the formation of more CO_2
C. a decrease in blood pH
D. an imbalance that can be treated with bicarbonate solution
E. all of the above

Answers

1. A 2. B 3. B 4. C 5. C 6. D 7. A 8. D 9. A 10. C
11. E 12. B 13. D 14. E 15. C 16. B 17. A 18. B 19. D 20. C
21. B 22. B 23. A 24. D 25. B 26. C 27. A 28. D 29. E 30. A

Chapter 9 – Solutions to Odd-Numbered Problems

Practice Problems

9.1   a. acid   b. base   c. acid   d. base

9.3   Most hydrogen atoms contain one proton, one electron, and no neutrons. Therefore, a positively charged hydrogen ion (H^+) is simply one proton.

9.5   a. HI is the acid (proton donor), and H_2O is the base (proton acceptor).
        b. H_2O is the acid (proton donor), and F^- is the base (proton acceptor).

9.7   The strong acids are: (a.) H_2SO_4 and (b.) HCl.

9.9   The strong bases are: (b.) KOH and (c.) LiOH.

9.11   Only a. HBr completely ionizes in water.

9.13   a. hydrobromic acid, HBr
        b. chloric acid, $HClO_3$
        c. nitrous acid, HNO_2

9.15   a. $HNO_3(aq) + LiOH(s) \rightarrow H_2O(l) + LiNO_3(aq)$

        b. $H_2SO_4(aq) + Ca(OH)_2(aq) \rightarrow 2H_2O(l) + CaSO_4(aq)$

9.17   a. $3HBr(aq) + Al(OH)_3(s) \rightarrow 3H_2O(l) + AlBr_3(aq)$

        b. $2HI(aq) + CaCO_3(s) \rightarrow H_2O(l) + CaI_2(aq) + CO_2(g)$

9.19   Reversible reactions are reactions that can proceed in both the forward and reverse directions.

9.21   a. $K = \dfrac{[CO_2][H_2]}{[CO][H_2O]}$ b. $K = \dfrac{[CH_3COO^-][H_3O^+]}{[CH_3COOH]}$

9.23   a. reactants
        b. products
        c. both reactants and products are present in equal amounts.

9.25   a. Shifts right (more products formed).   b. Shifts left (more reactants formed).
        c. Shifts right (more products formed).   d. Shifts left (more reactants formed).

9.27   a. Shifts left (more reactants formed).   b. Shifts right (more products formed.)
        c. Shifts right (more products formed).   d. Shifts left (more reactants formed).

9.29   The escape of CO_2 gas removes CO_2; equilibrium favors the formation of the products. The soda no longer bubbles.

9.31   a. $H_2PO_4^-$ b. HF   c. HBr

9.33   a. acid HSO_4^- conjugate base SO_4^{2-}
           base H_2O conjugate acid H_3O^+
        b. acid NH_4^+ conjugate base NH_3
           base H_2O conjugate acid H_3O^+
        c. acid HCN; conjugate base CN^-
           base NO_2^- conjugate acid HNO_2

9.35   a. F^- fluoride ion   b. OH^- hydroxide ion
        c. HCO_3^- bicarbonate ion   d. SO_4^{2-} sulfate ion

9.37   a. HCO_3^- bicarbonate ion   b. H_3O^+ hydronium ion
        c. H_3PO_4 phosphoric acid   d. HBr, hydrobromic acid

9.39 a.

$$HCOOH(aq) + H_2O(l) \rightleftharpoons HCOO^-(aq) + H_3O^+(l)$$

    Formic acid   Base   Conjugate   Conjugate
                                             base   acid

b.

$$H_2PO_4^-(aq) + H_2O(l) \rightleftharpoons HPO_4^{2-}(aq) + H_3O^+(aq)$$

    Acid   Base   Conjugate   Conjugate
                                       base   acid

c.

$$HCO_3^-(aq) + H_2O(l) \rightleftharpoons CO_3^{2-}(aq) + H_3O^+(aq)$$

    Acid   Base   Conjugate Conjugate
                                             base   acid

9.41 a. basic   b. acidic   c. basic   d. acidic

9.43 a. basic   b. acidic   c. basic   d. neutral

9.45 a. 7.92   b. 2.15   c. 10.33   d. 7.00

9.47 a. 7.9×10^{-13} M   b. 3×10^{-6} M   c. 1.0×10^{-2} M   d. 5×10^{-9} M

9.49 a. $H_2PO_4^-$ b. H_2SO_4 c. formic acid   d. ammonium ion

9.51 pyruvic acid

9.53 a. acid form, carboxylic acid
        b. equal
        c. conjugate base form, carboxylate

9.55 a.   b.   c.

         CH(CH$_3$)$_2$ CH(CH$_3$)$_2$ CH(CH$_3$)$_2$

$H_3N^+{-}C{-}C{-}OH$ $H_3N^+{-}C{-}C{-}O^-$ $H_2N{-}C{-}C{-}O^-$

          pH = 1.0   pH = 6.0   pH = 11.0

9.57 Lidocaine. In both cases, the pH < pK_a, yet because lidocaine's pK_a is closer to physiological pH, there will be more of the conjugate base (the neutral form) present and more will cross the nerve cells, becoming the active form.

9.59 a. Hyperventilation will lower the CO_2 level in the blood, which decreases the H_3O^+ and increases the blood pH.
        b. The equilibrium will shift to the left.
        c. This condition is called respiratory alkalosis.
        d. Breathing into a bag will increase the CO_2 level, which increases H_3O^+ (by shifting the equilibrium to the right), and lowers the blood pH.
        e. The equilibrium will shift to the right.

Additional Problems

9.61 a. strong   b. weak   c. strong   d. weak

9.63 Both strong and weak acids produce H_3O^+ in water. Weak acids are only slightly ionized, whereas a strong acid exists only as ions in solution (fully ionizes).

9.65 a. fluoride, F^- b. formate, $HCOO^-$ c. HSO_3^-, hydrogen sulfite, and SO_3^{2-}, sulfite

9.67   d.

9.69   a.

$$K = \frac{[H_2][I_2]}{[HI]^2}$$

b. HI predominates.

9.71   a. exothermic

b. $K = \dfrac{[CH_3OH]}{[CO][H_2]^2}$

c. It will shift to the right.
d. It will shift to the left.
e. It will shift to the right.

9.73   a. NO_2^- b. CH_3NH_2 c. $HCOO^-$

9.75   a. $CH_3CH(OH)COOH$ b. $CH_3NH_3^+$ c. HPO_4^{2-}

9.77   a. 7.60, basic   b. 1.15, acidic   c. 10.4, basic

9.79   a. $3.0\times10^{-4}\,M$ b. $1\times10^{-5}\,M$ c. $5.6\times10^{-10}\,M$

9.81   a. A buffer system keeps the pH constant.
b. The conjugate base CH_3COO^- from the salt $NaCH_3COO$ is needed to neutralize any added acid.
c. Added H_3O^+ reacts with CH_3COO^-.
d. Added OH^- reacts with CH_3COOH.

9.83   a. metabolic acidosis
b. below normal
c. administer bicarbonate $\left(HCO_3^-\right)$

9.85   a.   b.

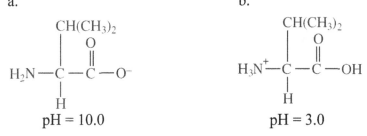

CH(CH₃)₂   CH(CH₃)₂
       O   O
       ‖   ‖
H₂N—C—C—O⁻   H₃N⁺—C—C—OH
       H   H
   pH = 10.0   pH = 3.0

Challenge Problems

9.87

H O
| ‖
H₂N—C—C—O⁻
|
H

9.89   a. right, forming more oxyhemoglobin
b. left, forming more deoxyhemoglobin
c. left, forming more deoxyhemoglobin

9.91   Number of moles of NaOH = number of moles of acetic acid

$$\frac{0.500 \text{ moles Na OH}}{1\,\cancel{L}} \times \frac{1\,\cancel{L}}{1000\,\cancel{ML}} \times 16.5\,\cancel{ML} = 0.00825 \text{ moles NaOH}$$

$$0.00825\,\cancel{\text{mole NaOH}} \times \frac{1 \text{ mole acetic acid}}{1\,\cancel{\text{mole NaOH}}} = 0.00825 \text{ mole acetic acid}$$

$$\frac{0.00825 \text{ mole acetic acid}}{10.0\,\cancel{mL}} \times \frac{1000\ ML}{1\,\cancel{L}} = 0.825\,M \text{ acetic acid}$$

Proteins — Workers of the Cell

Chapter 10

10.1 Amino Acids – A Second Look

Learning Objectives

Upon completion of this material, a student should be able to do the following:

A. Define the following key terms:

alpha (α) carbon

alpha (α) amino group

alpha (α) carboxylate group

nonpolar amino acids

polar amino acids

B. Draw the general structure of an amino acid.

C. Identify amino acids by their one-letter and three-letter abbreviations.

D. Identify amino acids based on their polarity.

10.2 Protein Formation

Learning Objectives

Upon completion of this material, a student should be able to do the following:

A. Define the following key terms:

amide

peptide bond

dipeptide

N-terminus

C-terminus

polypeptide

protein

B. Predict the products of a biological condensation or hydrolysis reaction, including peptide bond formation.

C. Form a peptide bond between amino acids.

10.3 The Three-Dimensional Structure of Proteins

Learning Objectives

Upon completion of this material, a student should be able to do the following:

A. Define the following key terms:

primary (1°) structure

protein backbone

secondary (2°) structure

alpha helix (α helix)

beta-pleated sheet (β–pleated sheet)

tertiary (3°) structure

nonpolar interactions

hydrophobic effect

polar interactions

salt bridges (ionic attractions)

disulfide bond

globular protein

fibrous protein

quaternary (4°) structure

B. Describe the attractive forces present as a protein folds into its three-dimensional shape.
C. Distinguish the levels of protein structure.

10.4 Denaturation of Proteins

Learning Objectives
Upon completion of this material, a student should be able to do the following:
    A. Define the following key term:

        denaturation
    B. List the causes of protein denaturation and the attractive forces affected.
    C. Distinguish protein denaturation and protein hydrolysis.

10.5 Protein Functions

Learning Objectives
Upon completion of this material, a student should be able to do the following:
    A. Define the following key terms:

hormone	**prosthetic group**
receptors	**conformational change**
integral membrane protein	**antigen**

    B. Identify various functions of proteins.
    C. Provide examples of protein structure dictating protein function.

10.6 Enzymes – Life's Catalysts

Learning Objectives
Upon completion of this material, a student should be able to do the following:
    A. Define the following key terms:

active site	**coenzyme**
substrate	**enzyme–substrate complex (ES)**
substrate specificity	**lock-and-key model**
cofactor	**induced-fit model**

    B. Define active site and substrate.
    C. Distinguish cofactor, coenzyme, and prosthetic group.
    D. Distinguish the lock-and-key model from the induced-fit model.
    E. Discuss factors that lower the activation energy and reaction speed for an enzyme-catalyzed reaction.

10.7 Factors That Affect Enzyme Activity

Learning Objectives
Upon completion of this material, a student should be able to do the following:
    A. Define the following key terms:

activity	**reversible inhibition**
steady state	**competitive inhibitors**
pH optimum	**noncompetitive inhibitors**
temperature optimum	**irreversible inhibition inhibitor**

    B. Describe how substrate concentration, pH, and temperature affect enzyme activity.
    C. Distinguish competitive, noncompetitive, and irreversible inhibition.

Practice Test for Chapter 10

1. The side chain in the following amino acid is a _____.

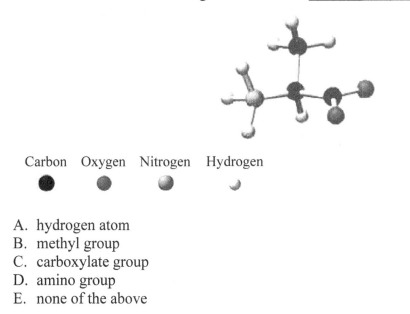

Carbon   Oxygen   Nitrogen   Hydrogen

A. hydrogen atom
B. methyl group
C. carboxylate group
D. amino group
E. none of the above

2. The following amino acid could be represented as _____.

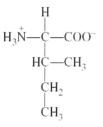

A. isoleucine
B. Ile
C. I
D. all of the above

3. How many chiral centers are present in the following amino acid?

$$H_3\overset{+}{N}\text{—}\overset{\displaystyle H}{\underset{\displaystyle HC\text{—}CH_3}{C}}\text{—}COO^-$$

$$\begin{array}{c} H \\ | \\ H_3\overset{+}{N}\text{—}C\text{—}COO^- \\ | \\ HC\text{—}CH_3 \\ | \\ CH_2 \\ | \\ CH_3 \end{array}$$

A. none
B. 1
C. 2
D. 3
E. 5

4. When amino acids react and form a peptide, _____.
   A. a condensation reaction occurs
   B. an amide bond forms
   C. the —COO⁻ of one amino acid reacts with the —NH₃⁺ of another amino acid
   D. both A and B
   E. A, B, and C

5. Consider the following structure.

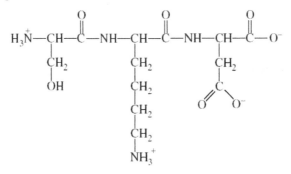

   This represents a _____ with _____ as the N-terminal amino acid and
   contains _____ amide bonds.
   A. tripeptide; serine; two
   B. tripeptide; aspartate; two
   C. dipeptide; Ser; three
   D. dipeptide; D; three

6. Consider the following structure.

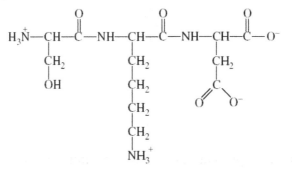

   Which of the following correctly describes this structure?
   A. Hydrolysis would produce three amino acids, all with nonpolar side chains.
   B. Hydrolysis would produce three amino acids, all with hydrophilic side chains.
   C. Hydrolysis would produce two amino acids, all with polar side chains.
   D. Hydrolysis would produce two amino acids, all with hydrophobic side chains.

7. The following peptide could be named as _____.

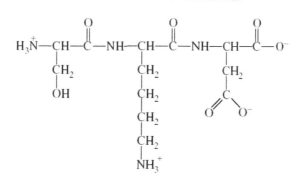

A. Ser—Lys—Asp
B. S—L—A
C. Asp—Lys—Ser
D. D—R—S
E. either A or B
F. either C or D

8. Consider the following.

    Asp—Lys—Ser—Asp—Arg—Val—Tyr—Ile—His—Pro—Phe—Ser—Lys—Asp

What level of protein structure is represented?
A. primary
B. secondary
C. tertiary
D. quaternary

9. When the following two peptides interact via hydrogen bonding, what level of protein structure is formed?

    Asp—Lys—Ser—Asp—Arg—Val—Tyr—Ile—His—Pro—Phe—Ser—Lys—Asp

    Tyr—Gln—Val—Asp—Ser—Lys—Thr—Pro—Ala—Val—Ile—Leu—Gln—Arg

A. primary
B. secondary
C. tertiary
D. quaternary

10. What level of protein structure is depicted in the following image?

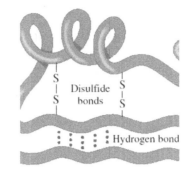

A. primary
B. secondary
C. tertiary
D. quaternary

11. Which level of protein structure does not usually involve hydrogen bonding?
A. primary
B. secondary
C. tertiary
D. quaternary

12. Consider the following description of protein structure:

"Open extended zigzag with amino acid side chains pointing upward and downward"

This description corresponds to a _____.
A. secondary structure called a β-pleated sheet
B. tertiary structure called a β-pleated sheet
C. secondary structure called an α helix
D. tertiary structure called an α helix

13. How many different tripeptides could be produced containing one glycine, one cysteine, and one glutamine?
A. 1
B. 2
C. 3
D. 4
E. 6
F. 8

14. The amino acid shown would most likely be involved in what type of interaction in the tertiary structure of protein?

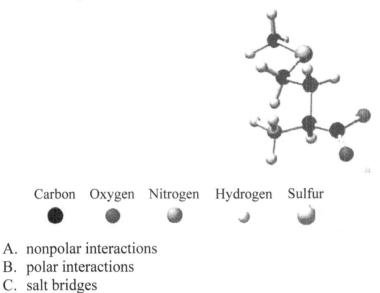

Carbon Oxygen Nitrogen Hydrogen Sulfur

A. nonpolar interactions
B. polar interactions
C. salt bridges
D. disulfide bridges

15. What type(s) of interaction(s) could occur between the side chains of the following pairs of amino acids?

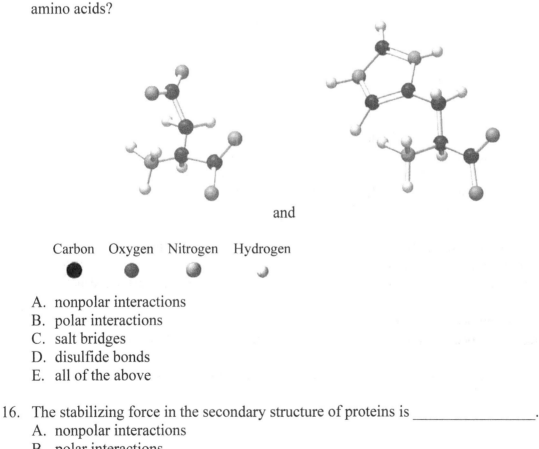

and

Carbon Oxygen Nitrogen Hydrogen

A. nonpolar interactions
B. polar interactions
C. salt bridges
D. disulfide bonds
E. all of the above

16. The stabilizing force in the secondary structure of proteins is _____.
A. nonpolar interactions
B. polar interactions
C. salt bridges
D. disulfide bridges
E. hydrogen bonding

17. Consider the following image.

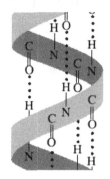

This excerpt represents a _____.
A. secondary protein structure stabilized by hydrogen bonds
B. primary protein structure stabilized by hydrogen bonds
C. secondary protein structure stabilized by salt bridges
D. tertiary protein structure stabilized by hydrogen bonds

18. The following represents an excerpt from a polypeptide chain:

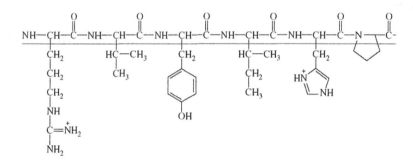

Which of the following correctly describes this image?
A. The underlined portion represents the protein backbone.
B. This is a representation of the primary structure of the protein.
C. The gray structures represent the protein's side chains.
D. All of the above are correct for this image.

19. When two —SH groups are brought close together when a protein folds, _____.
A. reduction can occur, forming a disulfide bond
B. oxidation can occur, forming an —S—S— link, which stabilizes the tertiary structure of the protein
C. oxidation can occur, forming a salt bridge
D. reduction can occur, which stabilizes the quaternary structure of the protein

20. Which of the following amino acids would be more likely to be on the interior of a protein after it has folded into its tertiary structure?
A. lysine
B. aspartate
C. tyrosine
D. phenylalanine

21. Which of the following is most likely to disrupt the hydrogen bonding in proteins?
    A. application of heat
    B. addition of an acid
    C. addition of a base
    D. presence of organic compounds

22. Which of the following denaturing agents would most likely to disrupt the stabilizing force represented here?

    A. addition of an acid
    B. heavy metals
    C. mechanical agitation
    D. both B and C

23. Consider the following depiction of a protein.

    This image could represent _____.
    A. hemoglobin
    B. an antibody
    C. collagen
    D. a glucose transporter

24. Consider the following depiction of the reaction between glucose and adenosine triphosphate.

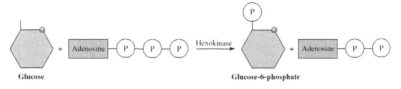

    In this reaction, _____.
    A. glucose-6-phosphate is the ES
    B. hexokinase is the enzyme
    C. adenosine triphosphate is a cofactor
    D. all of the above

25. Which of the following models of enzyme activity could be used to explain an enzyme that has more than one substrate?

A.

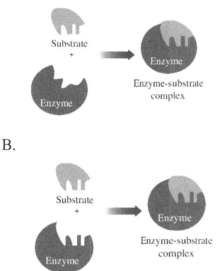

B.

C. Either one could be used.

D. Neither one would be used because enzymes are specific.

26. Carboxypeptidase A catalyzes the hydrolysis of peptide bonds. Zn^{2+} is needed in this hydrolysis. In this reaction, _____.

A. carboxypeptidase A is a coenzyme and Zn^{2+} is a cofactor

B. carboxypeptidase A is the enzyme and Zn^{2+} is a coenzyme

C. carboxypeptidase A is a cofactor and Zn^{2+} is a coenzyme

D. carboxypeptidase A is the enzyme and Zn^{2+} is a cofactor

27. The following image shows glucose and the enzyme hexokinase (the large molecule). Based on this diagram, _____.:

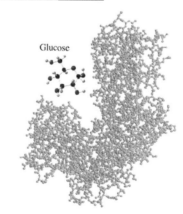

A. the crevice or pocket is the active site of hexokinase

B. the ES has not yet formed

C. the crevice or pocket might be lined with polar amino acids

D. the enzyme folding around glucose would be part of the induced-fit model

E. all of the above

28. Which of the following is **not** a factor in lowering the activation energy in the formation of ES?
    A. heat of reaction
    B. bond energy
    C. orientation
    D. proximity

29. Sucrase catalyzes the breakdown of sucrose to glucose and fructose in the small intestine with an optimum pH of 6.3. Which of the following will decrease the rate of catalysis?
    A. increase the pH
    B. decrease the H_3O^+ concentration
    C. increase the temperature to 65 °C
    D. all of the above

30. The structure on the left has been shown to inhibit the reaction of the substrate on the right.

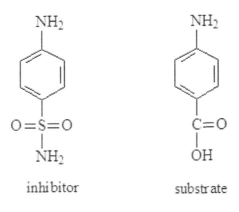

This is most likely an example of _____.
    A. reversible inhibition
    B. irreversible inhibition
    C. competitive inhibition
    D. noncompetitive inhibition
    E. A and C
    F. A and D

Answers

1. B 2. D 3. C 4. E 5. A 6. B 7. A 8. A 9. B 10. C
11. A 12. A 13. E 14. A 15. C 16. E 17. A 18. D 19. B 20. D
21. A 22. B 23. C 24. B 25. A 26. D 27. E 28. A 29. D 30. E

Chapter 10 – Solutions to Odd-Numbered Problems

Practice Problems

10.1   a.

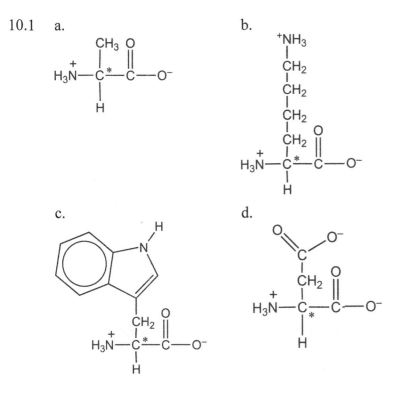

b.

c.

d.

10.3   a. Ala, A, hydrocarbon (no functional group)
        b. Lys, K, protonated amine
        c. Trp, W, aromatic
        d. Asp, D, carboxylate

10.5   a. nonpolar, hydrophobic   b. polar charged, hydrophilic   c. nonpolar, hydrophobic
        d. polar neutral, hydrophilic

10.7   a.

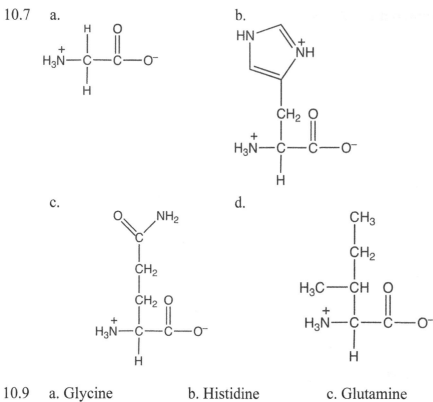

b.

c.   d.

10.9   a. Glycine   b. Histidine   c. Glutamine   d. Isoleucine

10.11

    a.

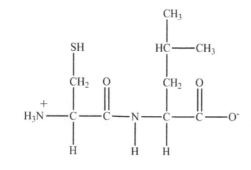

    b. $CH_3(CH_2)_{14}\ COOH\ +\ CH_3(CH_2)_{29}\ OH$

10.13   a.

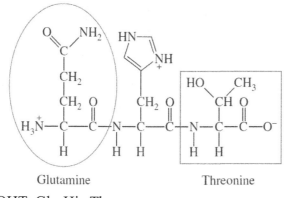

               Glutamine   Threonine

    b.   QHT, Gln-His-Thr

10.15 & 10.17

a.

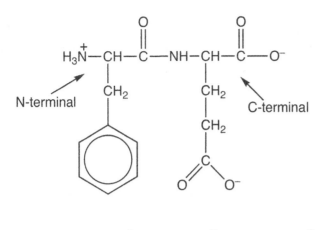

b.

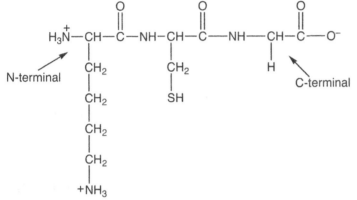

c.

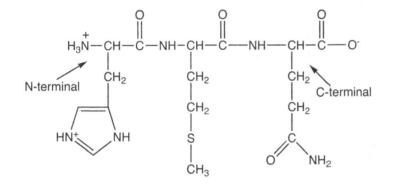

d.

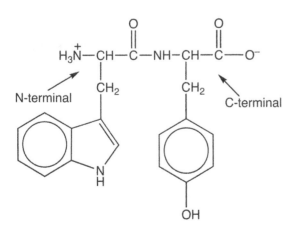

10.19   covalent bonding; peptide bond

10.21   hydrogen bonding

10.23   An α-helix is a coiled structure with the amino acid side chains protruding outward from the helix. The β-pleated sheet is an open, extended, zigzag structure with the side chains of the amino acids oriented above and below the sheet.

10.25   a. salt bridge   b. London force (nonpolar interaction)
        c. hydrogen bonding   d. hydrogen bonding and ion dipole

10.27   a. quaternary   b. secondary   c. tertiary   d. primary

10.29   Beta-amyloid proteins in a normal person fold into an alpha helix, whereas those in persons with Alzheimer's disease fold into beta strands.

10.31   a. ionic and hydrogen bonding; secondary, tertiary, and quaternary structure
        b. hydrogen bonding and London forces; secondary, tertiary, and quaternary structure

10.33   a. protein denaturation
        b. protein hydrolysis

10.35   collagen, structural connector
        hemoglobin, oxygen transporter
        antibody, bind foreign substances in body
        casein, storage protein

10.37   After a meal, the glucose transporter is active because glucose levels are high in the bloodstream and insulin is released. Upon waking up in the morning, the glucose transporter is less active because glucose and insulin levels in the bloodstream are low.

10.39   active site

10.41   tertiary

10.43   The induced-fit model. When glucose is fit into the active site, the enzyme undergoes a conformational change, closing around the substrate.

10. 45 Because the phosphates on ATP have negative charges and Mg^{2+} has positive charges, the attraction is ionic.

10.47   a. The enzyme activity will decrease if the temperature is raised above the optimum temperature.
        b. The activity will be lowered if the pH is changed.

10.49   a. no effect b. rate decreases

Additional Problems

10.51   carboxylate and protonated amine

10.53   a. tyrosine, Tyr
        b. proline, Pro
        c. cysteine, Cys

10.55   isoleucine, Ile, and threonine, Thr

10.57   Many possibilities; among them are rice and beans, peas and corn, oatmeal and peas, peas and rice.

10.59 a. 6

b. Gly-Pro-Lys, Gly-Lys-Pro, Pro-Gly-Lys, Pro-Lys-Gly, Lys-Pro-Gly, Lys-Gly-Pro

c.

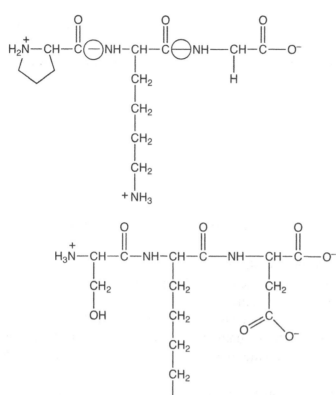

10.61 a.

b. This segment would be on the surface in the aqueous environment. The side chains are hydrophilic and would interact with the water in the surrounding environment.

10.63 a. Primary structures are held together by covalent bonding, and secondary structures are held together by hydrogen bond forces.

b. Complete proteins are those that contain all the essential amino acids, and incomplete proteins do not.

c. Fibrous proteins have elongated structures, and globular proteins have roughly spherical structures. Globular proteins are water soluble, but fibrous proteins are not.

10.65 a. quaternary structure

b. secondary structure

c. primary structure

d. tertiary and quaternary structure

10.67 a. α helix   b. α helix   c, α helix   d. β-sheet   e. both

10.69 a. hydrogen bonds and nonpolar attractions; secondary, tertiary, and quaternary

b. hydrogen bonds and salt bridges; secondary, tertiary, and quaternary

c. hydrogen bonds and nonpolar attractions; secondary, tertiary, and quaternary

10.71 disulfide bonds, thioglycolate

10.73 a. proline

b. An OH group is added to the side chain to form hydroxyproline.

c. The OH on the side chain allows for the formation of more hydrogen bonds between side chains, which increases the strength of the collagen.

10.75 The middle portion of these proteins spans the nonpolar portion of the membrane. This surface interacts with the nonpolar environment and, therefore, must be nonpolar itself.

10.77 The active site is the location on an enzyme where catalysis occurs.

10.79 a. (1) active site
       b. (3) induced-fit model
       c. (2) lock-and-key model
10.81 Because trypsin can have more than one substrate, its action is better described by the induced-fit model.
10.83 Since thiamine is an organic molecule involved in enzymatic reactions, but is not itself an enzyme, then it must be a coenzyme.
10.85 a. requires a cofactor
       b. describes a simple enzyme
       c. requires a coenzyme
10.87 a. (c) both
       b. (b) serve to hold the substrate
       c. (b) serve to hold the substrate
       d. (c) both
10.89 a. The rate would increase due to an increase of the probability of collision until a steady state is reached.
       b. The rate would decrease due to protein denaturation.
       c. The optimum temperature for trypsin is near body temperature, 37 °C. The rate would decrease due to slower movement of molecules.
10.91 The products do not fit snugly into the active site, so they are released.
10.93 An irreversible inhibitor forms bonds to the enzyme and permanently inactivates it. A reversible inhibitor temporarily inactivates the enzyme, but when the inhibitor is removed, the enzyme regains its activity.
10.95 If the amount of enzyme was increased in a reaction occurring at a steady state, the maximum rate of the reaction would increase since more enzyme is present to convert substrate into product.
10.97 Cadmium would be a noncompetitive inhibitor because increasing the substrate and cofactor has no effect on the rate. This implies that the cadmium is binding to another site on the enzyme.
10.99 When designing an inhibitor, usually the substrate of an enzyme is known even if the structure of the enzyme is not. It is easier to design a molecule that resembles the substrate (competitive) than to find an inhibitor that binds to a second site on an enzyme (noncompetitive).

Challenge Problems

10.101

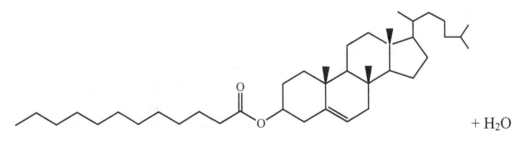

10.103 Both have nonpolar interiors and polar surfaces. On a micelle, the polar heads of the fatty acid salts face outward into the aqueous environment, similar to the polar amino acid side chains on the globular protein. The nonpolar tails of the fatty acid salts gather together in the interior of the micelle just as the nonpolar amino acid side chains gather in the interior of the globular protein.
10.105 a. The polar amino acids are likely involved in catalysis.
       b. The nonpolar amino acids are likely involved in aligning the substrate correctly.
       c. The substrate is likely nonpolar with a small polar portion.

Nucleic Acids
Big Molecules with a Big Role

Introduction

Learning Objectives
Upon completion of this material, a student should be able to do the following:
    A. Define the following key terms:

DNA	**gene**
genome	**RNA**

11.1 Components of Nucleic Acids

Learning Objectives
Upon completion of this material, a student should be able to do the following:
    A. Define the following key terms:

        nucleotide   **nucleoside**

    B. Distinguish the five nitrogenous bases found in nucleic acids as purine or pyrimidine.
    C. Identify the five nitrogenous bases found in nucleic acids by name.
    D. Distinguish the bases ribose and deoxyribose.
    E. Write condensation products for nucleoside and nucleotide formation.

11.2 Nucleic Acid Formation

Learning Objectives
Upon completion of this material, a student should be able to do the following:
    A. Define the following key terms:

        nucleic acid   **phosphodiester bond**

    B. Write the product of a condensation of nucleotides.
    C. Abbreviate a nucleic acid using one-letter base coding.
    D. Characterize the structural features of nucleic acids.

11.3 DNA

Learning Objectives
Upon completion of this material, a student should be able to do the following:
    A. Define the following key terms:

double helix	**supercoiling**
complementary base pair	**chromosome**

    B. Characterize the structural features of DNA.
    C. Write the complementary base pairs for a single strand of DNA.

11.4 RNA and Protein Synthesis

Learning Objectives

Upon completion of this material, a student should be able to do the following:
- A. Define the following key terms:

transcription	**rRNA**
mRNA	**translation**
RNA polymerase	**tRNA**
ribosome	**anticodon**
organelle	

- B. List the types of RNA and their role in protein synthesis.
- C. Distinguish transcription from translation.
- D. Translate a DNA strand into its complementary mRNA.

11.5 Putting It Together: The Genetic Code and Protein Synthesis

Learning Objectives

Upon completion of this material, a student should be able to do the following:
- A. Define the following key terms:

codon	**genetic code**

- B. Translate an mRNA sequence into a protein sequence using the genetic code.
- C. Translate a template DNA sequence into a protein sequence using the genetic code.

11.6 Genetic Mutations

Learning Objectives

Upon completion of this material, a student should be able to do the following:
- A. Define the following key terms:

mutation	**carcinogen**
silent mutation	**somatic cell**
spontaneous mutation	**germ cell**
mutagen	**genetic disease**

- B. Define genetic mutation.
- C. Determine changes in protein sequence if an mRNA sequence is mutated.

11.7 Viruses

Learning Objectives

Upon completion of this material, a student should be able to do the following:
- A. Define the following key terms:

host	**envelope**
capsid	**retrovirus**
nucleoside analog	

- B. List the differences between a virus and a cell.
- C. List the structural components of a virus.
- D. Describe how a virus infects a cell.

11.8 Recombinant DNA Technology

Learning Objectives
Upon completion of this material, a student should be able to do the following:

A. Define the following key terms:

recombinant DNA	**plasmid**
restriction enzyme	**expression**
vector	

B. Apply knowledge of nucleic acid structure to DNA technology.

Practice Test for Chapter 11

1. Examine the following substance. This substance is the _____.

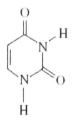

A. purine base uracil
B. pyrimidine base uracil
C. purine base thymine
D. pyrimidine base thymine

2. The following substance is classified as _____.

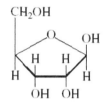

A. a purine
B. a pyrimidine
C. ribose
D. deoxyribose

3. If a condensation reaction occurred between the following two substances, the type of product formed would be _____.

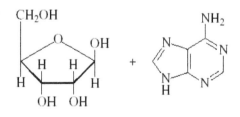

A. DNA
B. a nucleotide
C. a nucleoside
D. RNA

4. What is the name of the product of the following reaction?

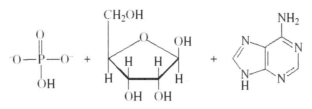

A. adenosine-5′-monophosphate
B. adenosine nucleotide
C. adenosine phosphate
D. AMP
E. A or D

5. Where is the following substance usually found?

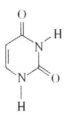

A. RNA
B. DNA
C. both DNA and RNA
D. neither DNA nor RNA

6. The difference between CMP and dCMP is found in which component of their molecular structure?
A. sugar
B. phosphate
C. nitrogenous base
D. the bonds linking the components together

7. Consider the following structure.

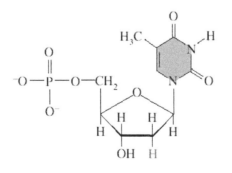

This represents _____.
A. an RNA nucleotide
B. uridine-5′-monophosphate
C. TMP
D. dTMP

8. Which of the following correctly describes the structure of a nucleic acid?
   A. The repeating unit is a nucleoside.
   B. The backbone repeat unit is: sugar–base–phosphate.
   C. One-letter abbreviation is the name of the sugar.
   D. Free left end is designated as 5′.
   E. All of these are correct.

9. Consider the following structure.

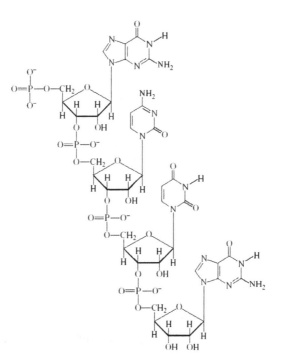

   Which of the following is correct?
   A. has pyrimidine bases at the 5′ and 3′ ends
   B. contains 4 phosphodiester bonds
   C. contains 4 nucleotides
   D. could be found in DNA
   E. All of the above are correct.

10. What is the abbreviation for the following structure?

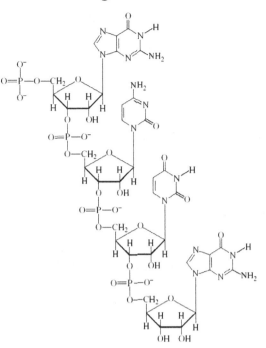

    A. 5'GCUG3'
    B. 5'GUCG3'
    C. 5'GUTG3'
    D. 5'GAUG3'

11. The nucleic acid analog of the N-terminus of a protein is _____.
    A. a nucleotide
    B. the 5' end
    C. the 3' end
    D. a phosphodiester bond

12. The double-helix structure of DNA is stabilized by _____.
    A. phosphodiester bonds
    B. covalent bonds
    C. hydrogen bonds
    D. disulfide bridges

13. Which of the following is **not** a complementary base pair found in DNA?
    A. A and T
    B. G and C
    C. A and U
    D. All are complementary DNA base pairs.

14. What is the complementary DNA segment 3′ to 5′ for the following segment?

5′GGCTTA3′

A. 3′ATTCGG5′
B. 3′GGCTTA5′
C. 3′TAAGCC5′
D. 3′CCGAAT5′

15. Which of the following constitutes a difference between DNA and RNA?
A. sugar present
B. strand structure
C. size
D. complementary base of adenine
E. All of the above are differences.

16. Which base in mRNA complements the base represented as "A" in DNA?
A. T
B. U
C. G
D. C

17. The sequence of bases in a DNA template is as follows:

5′ATCGAT3′

What is the corresponding mRNA that is produced from this DNA?
A. 3′TAGCTA5′
B. 3′ATCGAT5′
C. 3′UAGCUA5′
D. 3′AUCGAU5′

18. Which type of RNA provides the amino acids for the growing peptide chain?
A. tRNA
B. mRNA
C. rRNA
D. none of the above

19. The synthesis of a protein based on a DNA template is called _____.
A. translocation
B. transcription
C. translation
D. transmutation

20. What do the following mRNA codons have in common?

UAA   UAG   UGA

A. They stop protein synthesis.
B. They start protein synthesis.
C. They code for the same amino acid.
D. They have nothing in common.

21. What is the sequence of amino acids coded by the following codons in mRNA?

5′ CCA|GUC|AAA|GCC 3′

A. Ala—Lys—Val—Pro
B. Pro—Lys—Val—Ala
C. Pro—Val—Lys—Ala
D. Ala—Val—Lys—Pro

22. The conversion of the information on the codons in mRNA to a peptide chain occurs
_____.

A. in the nucleus of the cell
B. on the nuclear membrane
C. in the cytoplasm
D. in the ribosome

23. Consider the following representation of tRNA.

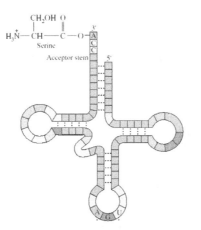

This tRNA is a complement to what codon on mRNA?
A. 5′AGU3′
B. 5′UCA3′
C. 5′TCA3′
D. 5′ACU3′

24. Which of the following represents the correct sequence of events in protein synthesis?
A. transcription, activation, translation, termination
B. transcription, activation, termination, translation
C. translation, activation, transcription, termination
D. activation, transcription, translation, termination

25. Consider the following segment of DNA.

3′ GGG|TTA|CAC|ATT 5′

What amino acids will be placed in the peptide chain from this segment?
A. Val—Asn—Pro
B. Pro—Asn—Val—Tyr
C. Pro—Asn—Val
D. Val—Leu—His—Ile

26. If a codon in mRNA was changed from UGU to UGC, this change could most specifically be called a _____.
    A. mutagen
    B. mutation
    C. silent mutation
    D. carcinogen

27. A normal DNA template produces the following mRNA sequence:

    5′ACU|UAC|CGG3′

    Consider that a change in the DNA template changes the mRNA sequence to the following:

    5′ACU|UAG|CGG3′

    How would this change affect the protein produced?
    A. silent mutation
    B. mutation affecting protein structure/function
    C. no effect at all
    D. cannot predict with the given information

28. Which of the following is **not** a property of all viruses?
    A. utilize the ribosomes of the infected cells
    B. contain nucleic acids enclosed in a capsid
    C. can infect any cell type
    D. consist of small particles with 3–200 genes
    E. All of the above are properties of all viruses.

29. Which of the following correctly pertains to the HIV-1 virus and current therapies?
    A. HIV-1 is a retrovirus.
    B. Nucleoside analogs are competitive inhibitors.
    C. Protease inhibitors halt transcription.
    D. Current research involves the use of mutagens.

30. In recombinant DNA technology, the production of a nonnative protein is called a(n) _____.

    A. vector
    B. somatic cell
    C. expression
    D. restriction enzyme

Answers

1. B 2. C 3. C 4. E 5. A 6. A 7. D 8. D 9. C 10. A
11. B 12. C 13. C 14. D 15. E 16. B 17. C 18. A 19. C 20. A
21. C 22. D 23. B 24. A 25. C 26. C 27. B 28. E 29. A 30. C

Practice Problems

11.1   a. purine: Adenine   b. pyrimidine: Cytosine

11.3   a. both DNA and RNA   b. both DNA and RNA

11.5   Ribose contains –OH on C2′, whereas deoxyribose contains only –H on C2′.

11.7   deoxyadenosine-5′-monophosphate (dAMP), deoxythymidine-5′-monophosphate (dTMP), deoxycytidine-5′-monophosphate (dCMP), deoxyguanosine-5′-monophosphate (dGMP)

11.9   a.

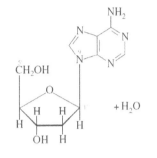

b.

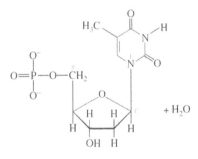

11.11   The nucleotides in nucleic acids are held together by phosphodiester bonds between the 3′-OH of a sugar (ribose or deoxyribose) and a phosphate group on the 5′-carbon of another sugar.

11.13

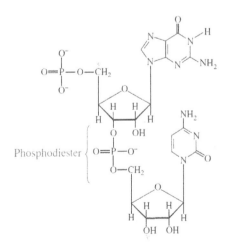

11.15   The two strands of nucleic acid that make up DNA are oriented in opposite directions (antiparallel) to each other. In one of the strands, the sugars are connected from 3′ C to 5′ C, and in the other strand they run 5′ to 3′.

11.17   The two DNA strands are held together by hydrogen bonds between the bases in each strand.

11.19 a. 3′TTTT5′

b. 3′GGGGAAAA5′

c. 3′TGTAACC5′

d. 3′ACACTTGG5′

11.21

	Protein	Nucleic Acid
Primary structure	Sequence of amino acids	Sequence of nucleotides
Secondary structure	Local hydrogen bonding between backbone atoms.	Hydrogen bonding between bases in nucleic acid strands
Tertiary structure	Folding of backbone associating amino acids far away in sequence.	Supercoiling of DNA into tight, compact structures like chromosomes.

11.23 Messenger RNA (mRNA): It contains a base sequence complementary to the DNA strand that encodes for proteins. It copies DNA and then moves from the nucleus to the ribosome.

Ribosomal RNA (rRNA): This is the structural component of the ribosome where proteins are manufactured in the cell.

Transfer RNA (tRNA): It is used in the ribosome to place a specific amino acid in the growing protein chain.

11.25 In transcription, the sequence of nucleotides on one strand of a DNA template (the double helix is temporarily unwound) is used to produce a complementary mRNA copy using the enzyme RNA polymerase.

11.27 3′AUGCCGUUCGAU5′

11.29 There are 20 amino acids, so there must be at least 20 different tRNAs.

11.31 a. Lys–Pro–Leu–Ala

b. Pro–Arg–Ser–Pro–Stop

c. Met–His–Lys–Glu–Val–Leu

11.33 Translocation is the movement of the second tRNA to the spot vacated by the first tRNA, allowing the next tRNA to bind to the ribosome. The amino acid is added to the growing peptide.

11.35 a. 5′ACA|CCC|CAA|UAA3′

b. 3′UGU|GGG|GUU|AUU5′

c. three-letter code: Thr–Pro–Gln–Stop

one-letter code: TPQ–Stop

11.37 A mutation is any change to the DNA sequence of a gene.

11.39 a. three-letter code: Leu–Lys–Arg–Val, one-letter code: LKRV

b. three-letter code: Ile–Lys–Arg–Val, one-letter code: IKRV

Changing leucine to isoleucine, which are both nonpolar, will probably have no effect on the protein function.

c. Nothing. Both codons code for arginine.

d. Leucine will be the last amino acid incorporated into the growing protein chain because UAA is a stop codon.

e. If an A is added to the beginning of the chain, the new mRNA would be:
5′ACU|UAA|ACG|AGU3′.

The amino acid sequence would be: Thr–Stop-Thr-Ser (T-Stop-T-S); the chain would stop after the first threonine.

f. If C is removed from the beginning of the chain, the new mRNA would be:
5′UUA|AAC|GAG3′.

The new amino acid sequence would be: Leu–Asn–Glu (LNE).

11.41   a. both   b. cell   c. virus

11.43   Viruses cannot replicate themselves without a host cell. They do not have the cell machinery (enzymes, organelles, etc.).

11.45   A vaccine allows the body to mount an immune response, by producing antibodies, to a less active form of the virus. Then, if an active form of the virus is encountered later, the body can fight against it more effectively.

11.47   Protease inhibitors inactivate an HIV-1 specific protease that is needed to process viral proteins.

11.49   Gene expression is producing a protein from a DNA gene sequence (usually of a nonnative gene).

11.51   A vector is a transporter for donor DNA. It enables the incorporation of the donor DNA into the organism DNA.

11.53   Restriction enzymes are used to cut the gene to be cloned out of the original DNA.

Additional Problems

11.55   a. pyrimidine   b. purine   c. pyrimidine
        d. pyrimidine   e. purine

11.57   a. cytosine, ribose
        b. adenine, deoxyribose
        c. guanine, deoxyribose
        d. uracil, ribose

11.59   Thymine contains a methyl ($-CH_3$) group at carbon-5 that uracil lacks.

11.61

	Protein	Nucleic Acid
Repeating unit	amino acid	nucleotide
Backbone repeat	$N–C_\alpha–C–N–C_\alpha–C$, etc.	sugar-phosphate-sugar-phosphate-etc.
One-letter abbreviation	name of amino acid	name of base
Free left end	amino or N terminus	5′ end
Free right end	carboxy or C terminus	5′ end

11.63   a. 3′AATGCCTGGCG5′
        b. 3′TATCGGGAATGACC5′
        c. 3′CCGGATGGAATTGCTGC5′

11.65   a. mRNA   b. tRNA   c. rRNA

11.67   a. GUU, GUC, GUA, GUG
        b. CCU, CCC, CCA, CCG
        c. CAU, CAC

11.69   a. leucine   b. arginine   c. isoleucine

11.71   a. Gly–Ile–Tyr–Arg
        b. Leu–Ser–Phe–Asn–Trp
        c. Val–Arg–Arg–Leu–Pro–Thr

11.73   three-letter code for Met-enkephalin: Tyr–Gly–Gly–Phe–Met, one-letter code: YGGFM

11.75   a. CAC   b. GGG   c. CUU

11.77 a. Both alanine and leucine have small, nonpolar R-groups. Both amino acids are found in similar environments in proteins, so this substitution is unlikely to affect protein structure or function.

b. If a serine codon (UCA) is replaced with a stop codon (UAA), the serine and remaining amino acids will not be added to the growing polypeptide chain. This can affect both the structure and function of the protein.

11.79 a. The development of nucleoside analogs that can be incorporated into viral DNA to stop reverse transcription is viable.

b. Integrase is a viral-only enzyme, so this would be a viable method for inactivating the virus.

c. Since RNA polymerase is used to make all proteins in the cell, this would not be a viable method to inactivate the virus.

11.81 Entry-point inhibitors block sites on the outside of a host cell where a virus would attach and eventually enter. If the virus cannot enter the cell, the virus cannot replicate.

11.83 When the gene sequence for GFP is linked to the recombined gene, it can be used to visually confirm the presence of recombined DNA.

Challenge Problems

11.85 a. 39

b. Answers will vary slightly depending on the codon selected.
5′AGU|UAU|AGU|AUG|CAA|CAU|UUU|CGU|UGG|GGU|AAA|CCU|GUU3′

c. Answers should complement the answer in part b.
3′ TCA|ATA|TCA|TAC|GTT|GTA|AAA|GCA|ACC|CCA|TTT|GGA|CAA5′

11.87 3 nucleotides/amino acid + 1 start condon + 1 stop codon =
(35 amino acids × 3) + 3 + 3 = 111 nucleotides

Food as Fuel — An Overview of Metabolism

Introduction

Learning Objectives
Upon completion of this material, a student should be able to do the following:
    A. Define the following key terms:

        metabolism   **metabolic pathway**

12.1 How Metabolism Works

Learning Objectives
Upon completion of this material, a student should be able to do the following:
    A. Define the following key terms:

metabolite	**anabolism**
*bio***chemical reactions**	**cytoplasm**
metabolic pathway	**cytosol**
catabolism	**mitochondrion**

    B. Distinguish catabolism from anabolism.
    C. Identify reactions as catabolic or anabolic.
    D. Name the parts of a cell associated with metabolism.

12.2 Metabolically Relevant Nucleotides

Learning Objectives
Upon completion of this material, a student should be able to do the following:
    A. Identify the metabolically relevant nucleotides.
    B. Distinguish the low-energy/high-energy oxidized/reduced forms of the relevant nucleotides.

12.3 Digestion— From Fuel Molecules to Hydrolysis Products

Learning Objectives
Upon completion of this material, a student should be able to do the following:
    A. Define the following key terms:

digestion	**chylomicrons**
emulsification	

    B. Compare digestion of carbohydrates, lipids, and proteins.

12.4 Glycolysis– From Hydrolysis Products to Common Metabolites

Learning Objectives
Upon completion of this material, a student should be able to do the following:
A. Define the following key terms:

gluconeogenesis
aerobic
anaerobic

oxidative decarboxylation
fermentation

B. Follow a molecule of glucose through the 10 reactions of glycolysis.
C. Discuss anaerobic and aerobic fates of pyruvate.
D. Contrast glycolysis for glucose and for fructose.

12.5 The Citric Acid Cycle – Central Processing

Learning Objectives
Upon completion of this material, a student should be able to do the following:
A. Define the following key term:

citric acid cycle

B. Identify the reactions in the citric acid cycle.
C. List the energy output of the citric acid cycle

12.6 Electron Transport and Oxidative Phosphorylation

Learning Objectives
Upon completion of this material, a student should be able to do the following:
A. Define the following key terms:

oxidative phosphorylation
chemiosmotic model

electrochemical gradient
thermogenesis

B. Describe the function of each enzyme complex (I–IV) during electron transport.
C. Discuss the function of coenzyme Q and cytochrome c.
D. Describe the production of ATP at complex V using the chemiosmotic model.

12.7 ATP Production

Learning Objectives
Upon completion of this material, a student should be able to do the following:
A. Convert the number of reduced nucleotides produced (NADH, $FADH_2$) to a corresponding number of ATP.
B. Calculate the number of ATP produced during the oxidative catabolism of a molecule of glucose.

12.8 Other Fuel Choices

Learning Objectives

Upon completion of this material, a student should be able to do the following:

A. Define the following key terms:

beta oxidation (β oxidation)	**ketosis**
fatty acyl CoA	**transamination**
ketone bodies	**urea cycle**

B. Calculate the number of ATP produced from a saturated fatty acid undergoing β oxidation.

C. Describe the metabolic pathways of β oxidation, production of ketone bodies, and the urea cycle.

Practice Test for Chapter 12

1. Which of the following reactions would **not** be classified as catabolic?

    A. $ADP + P_i + Energy \longrightarrow ATP$

    B. $Protein + H_2O \xrightarrow[Enzyme]{H^+} Amino\ acids$

    C. $Maltose + H_2O \xrightarrow{Maltase} Glucose + glucose$

    D. $C_6H_{12}O_6 + 6O_2 \longrightarrow 6CO_2 + 6H_2O$

2. Consider the substances listed in the following choices. Which would be classified as a metabolite?

    A. lactose
    B. carbon dioxide
    C. pyruvate
    D. ATP
    E. All are metabolites.

3. Consider the following statements. Which could be used to describe both catabolic and anabolic reactions?

    A. Involve oxidation reactions.
    B. Involve condensation reactions.
    C. Involve exergonic reactions.
    D. Involve enzyme catalyzed reactions.

4. How is the oxidized form of nicotinamide adenine dinucleotide represented?

    A. $FADH_2$
    B. NADH
    C. FAD
    D. NAD^+
    E. ADP

5. Which of the following is a characteristic of acetyl CoA?

    A. contains a thioester functional group
    B. is the high-energy form of coenzyme A
    C. exchanges energy when a C—S bond is hydrolyzed
    D. A and B
    E. A, B, and C

6. What is the abbreviation used to designate the following substance?

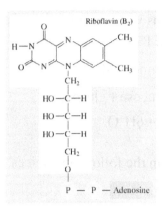

Riboflavin (B₂)

A. ATP
B. FAD
C. NAD⁺
D. FADH₂
E. Co A
F. Acetyl CoA

7. Consider the following reaction:

Lactase

Lactose → Galactose + Glucose

This reaction _____.
A. occurs in the stomach
B. is classified as a condensation reaction
C. produces products that can be transported in the bloodstream
D. represents emulsification

8. During the digestion of fats, which of the following transports the triglycerides from the stomach through the bloodstream?
A. chylomicron
B. bile salts
C. cholesterol
D. micelles

9. Of the following reactions, which occurs in the stomach?
   A.

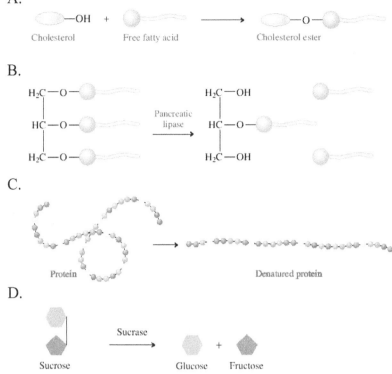

   B.

   C.

   D.

10. The end product of the digestion of starch is _____.
    A. cholesterol
    B. amino acids
    C. sucrose
    D. glucose

11. The following reaction represents the net chemical reaction of _____.

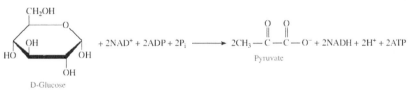

    A. glycolysis
    B. the citric acid cycle
    C. electron transport
    D. oxidative phosphorylation
    E. all of the above

12. In terms of **high-energy molecules**, what is the net output from two molecules of glucose during glycolysis?
    A. 2 ATP
    B. 2 ATP, 2 NADH
    C. 4 ATP, 2 NADH
    D. 4 ATP, 4 NADH
    E. 6 ATP, 6 NADH

13. Which of the following is produced during the aerobic oxidation of pyruvate?
    A. lactate
    B. acetyl CoA
    C. ethanol
    D. All are produced during aerobic oxidation.

14. Fructose can enter into glycolysis _____.
    A. as fructose-6-phosphate
    B. as dihydroxyacetone phosphate
    C. as glyceraldehyde-3-phosphate
    D. after the regulatory step
    E. all of the above

15. After 3 molecules of acetyl CoA move through the citric acid cycle, _____ are produced.
    A. 3 molecules of NADH
    B. 6 molecules of $FADH_2$
    C. 6 molecules of CO_2
    D. 6 molecules of GTP

16. In order for the citric acid cycle to run, which of the following is needed?
    A. pyruvate and oxaloacetate
    B. acetyl CoA and pyruvate
    C. acetyl CoA and citrate
    D. oxaloacetate and acetyl CoA

17. What do the following two steps in the citric acid cycle have in common?

    Reaction 3: isocitrate $\longrightarrow$ α-ketoglutarate

    Reaction 8: malate $\longrightarrow$ oxaloacetate

    A. reduction of NAD^+
    B. production of CO_2
    C. decarboxylation
    D. isomerization
    E. reduction of FAD

18. Which of the following reaction types is not involved in the citric acid cycle?
    A. hydrogenation
    B. hydrolysis
    C. dehydrogenation
    D. isomerization

19. All of the following are involved in electron transport **except** _____.
    A. cytochrome c
    B. QH_2
    C. ADP
    D. $FADH_2$

20. The process of producing energy from the oxidation of reduced nucleotides is termed
    _____.

    A. electron transport
    B. oxidative phosphorylation
    C. oxidative decarboxylation
    D. dehydrogenation

21. In the chemiosmotic model, which of the following drives the following reaction?

$$ADP + P_i + energy \longrightarrow ATP$$

    A. transfer of electrons from complex I to complex II
    B. release of H^+ during the oxidation of NADH and $FADH_2$
    C. reduction of O_2 to form water
    D. movement of H^+ through complex V

22. Electron transport occurs in the _____.
    A. cytosol
    B. mitochondrial matrix
    C. inner membrane of the mitochondria
    D. cell membrane

23. Which of the following describes the electron transport chain?
    A. NADH enters at complex I.
    B. $FADH_2$ enters at complex II.
    C. Water is produced at complex IV.
    D. ATP is produced at complex V.
    E. All of the above are correct descriptions.

24. For the oxidation of one molecule of glucose, which of the following produces the largest amount of ATP?
    A. glycolysis
    B. oxidation of pyruvate
    C. the citric acid cycle
    D. All produce approximately equal amounts.

25. The net production of ATP from NADH is greater than that from $FADH_2$ because
    _____.

    A. it takes two hydrogen atoms to reduce FAD.
    B. NADH enters the electron transport chain earlier than $FADH_2$.
    C. NADH pumps 6 protons into the inner mitochondrial membrane space while $FADH_2$ pumps 4 protons.
    D. A and C
    E. None of the above, $FADH_2$ produces more ATP per molecule.

26. Which of the following conversions directly produces the highest yield of ATP as a product of the reaction as written?

    A. glucose ⟶ 2 pyruvate

    B. pyruvate ⟶ lactate

    C. GTP ⟶ GDP + P$_i$

    D. pyruvate ⟶ acetyl CoA

27. Calculate the number of ATPs produced from the β oxidation of the following fatty acid entering β oxidation as an acyl CoA.

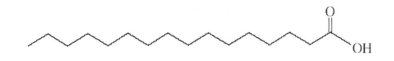

    A. 80 ATP
    B. 97.5 ATP
    C. 108 ATP
    D. 112 ATP

28. The following are the four steps involved in β oxidation. In which is the length of the fatty acyl CoA reduced by two carbon atoms?
    A. 1—oxidation
    B. 2—hydration
    C. 3—oxidation
    D. 4—removal of acetyl CoA
    E. None of the steps reduce the length by only two carbon atoms.

29. Which of the following characterizes the condition known as ketosis?
    A. accumulation of β-hydroxybutyrate, acetoacetate, and acetone in liver
    B. occurs in the presence of high concentration of carbohydrates
    C. low-fat levels in the diet
    D. high blood pH

30. During metabolism, all but which of the following characterize amino acids?
    A. undergo transamination before excretion
    B. have the ability to directly generate ATP
    C. eventually excretes nitrogen content as urea
    D. can regenerate intermediates in the citric acid cycle

Answers

1. A   2. C   3. D   4. D   5. E   6. B   7. C   8. A   9. C   10. D
11. A   12. D   13. B   14. E   15. C   16. D   17. A   18. A   19. C   20. B
21. D   22. C   23. E   24. C   25. B   26. A   27. C   28. D   29. A   30. B

Chapter 12 – Solutions to Odd-Numbered Problems

Practice Problems

12.1 In metabolism, a catabolic reaction breaks apart molecules, releases energy, and is an oxidation.

12.3 a. catabolism b. anabolism

12.5 hydrolysis

12.7 the mitochondrion

12.9 a. FAD/FADH$_2$ b. Acetyl CoA

12.11 a. NADH b. Acetyl CoA c. FAD

12.13 a. starch b. none c. starch, oligosaccharides, disaccharides

12.15 Cholesterol is esterified and packaged into lipoproteins.

12.17 amino acids

12.19 d-glucose

12.21 4 ATP (net 2 ATP)

12.23 2 NADH and 2 ATP

12.25 NAD$^+$

12.27 ethanol, CO$_2$ and NAD$^+$

12.29 The main regulation point of glycolysis is phosphofructokinase, the enzyme involved in step 3. Because the products of the metabolism of fructose enter glycolysis at step 5, they bypass the main regulation point, which leads to the production of excess pyruvate and acetyl CoA that is not needed in the cells and is ultimately converted to fat.

12.31 acetyl CoA and oxaloacetate

12.33 isocitrate → α-ketoglutarate (reaction 3) and α-ketoglutarate → succinyl CoA (reaction 4)

12.35 isocitrate → α-ketoglutarate (reaction 3), α-ketoglutarate → succinyl CoA (reaction 4), and

malate → oxaloacetate (reaction 8)

12.37 6 ATP, 6 NADH, and 2 FADH$_2$

12.39 coenzyme Q

12.41 complex IV

12.43 up to two: only one

12.45 As protons flow through ATP synthase, energy is released to produce ATP.

12.47 a. 2.5 ATP b. 7 ATP c. 5 ATP d. 10 ATP

12.49 mitochondrial matrix

12.51 a. and b.

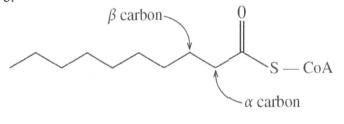

c.

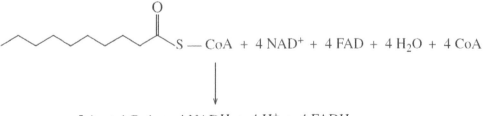

5 Acetyl CoA + 4 NADH + 4 H$^+$ + 4 FADH$_2$

12.53 Ketone bodies form when excess acetyl CoA results from the breakdown of large amounts of fat.

12.55 NH_4^+ is toxic if it accumulates in the body.

12.57 a. pyruvate   b. oxaloacetate, fumarate
       c. succinyl CoA   d. α-ketoglutarate

Additional Problems

12.59 a. cytosol
       b. mitochondrial matrix
       c. mitochondrial matrix

12.61 a. anabolic   b. anabolic

12.63 a. carbohydrate   b. fat   c. carbohydrate
       d. fat   e. protein

12.65 Lactose undergoes digestion in the small intestine to yield galactose and glucose.

12.67 a. produces ATP   b. neither   c. produces ATP

12.69 b. glucose-6-phosphate to fructose-6-phosphate

12.71 The runner's muscles may be switching over to anaerobic catabolism to keep ATP production going. The muscles produce lactate and H^+ during this process, causing soreness.

12.73 anaerobic (low-oxygen) conditions

12.75 a. citrate and isocitrate

       b. α-ketoglutarate

       c. isocitrate $\rightarrow \alpha$-ketoglutarate (reaction 3), α-ketoglutarate $\rightarrow$ succinyl CoA (reaction 4),

          succinate $\rightarrow$ fumarate (reaction 6), and malate $\rightarrow$ oxaloacetate (reaction 8)

       d. isocitrate $\rightarrow \alpha$-ketoglutarate (reaction 3), and malate $\rightarrow$ oxaloacetate (reaction 8)

12.77 O_2 is used during electron transport. The coenzymes NADH and $FADH_2$ produced in the citric acid cycle are oxidized to FAD and NAD^+ during electron transport.

12.79 a. oxidized   b. reduced   c. reduced

12.81 matrix, intermembrane space

12.83 Energy is released as protons flow down a concentration gradient through ATP synthase back to the matrix; energy is released and utilized for the synthesis of ATP.

12.85 The oxidation of glucose to pyruvate produces 7 ATP, 5 of which come from NADH, whereas 32 ATP are produced from the complete oxidation of glucose to CO_2 and H_2O.

12.87 a. 5   b. 4   c. 66 ATP

Challenge Problems

12.89 Oxidation of pyruvate: pyruvate → acetyl CoA

Reaction 3 of citric acid cycle: isocitrate → α-ketoglutarate

Reaction 4 of the citric acid cycle: α-ketoglutarate → succinyl CoA

12.91 a. and b.

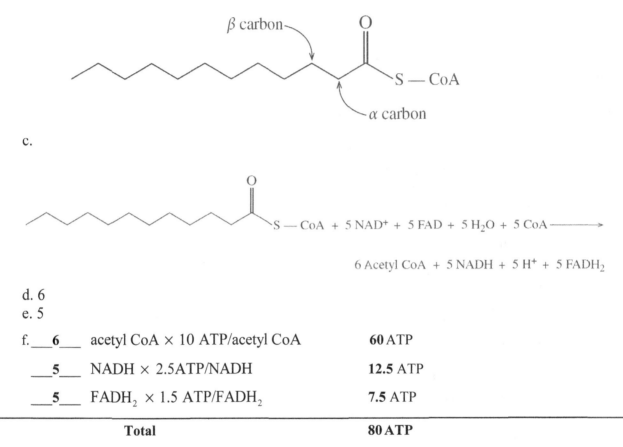

c.

d. 6
e. 5

f.___6___ acetyl CoA × 10 ATP/acetyl CoA   **60 ATP**

___5___ NADH × 2.5ATP/NADH   **12.5 ATP**

___5___ FADH$_2$ × 1.5 ATP/FADH$_2$ **7.5 ATP**

Total   **80 ATP**

12.93 Only oxaloacetate or pyruvate are starting points for gluconeogenesis. Acetyl CoA cannot be converted to pyruvate, so fatty acids cannot generate glucose.